Fact files

FISH

JOHN DAWES

with Amy-Jane Beer
and David Alderton

**CHARTWELL
BOOKS, INC.**

Published by
CHARTWELL BOOKS, INC.
A Division of **BOOK SALES, INC.**
114 Northfield Avenue
Edison, New Jersey 08837

The Brown Reference Group plc
8 Chapel Place
Rivington Street
London EC2A 3DQ
www.brownreference.com

ISBN 0-7858-1970-3

Editorial Director: Lindsey Lowe

Project Director: Graham Bateman

Art Director: Steve McCurdy

Editors: Derek Hall, Virginia Carter

Artists: Denys Ovenden, Norman Arlott, Ad Cameron with
        Trevor Boyer, Robert Gillmor, Peter Harrison,
        Sean Milne, Ian Willis

Printed in China

Contents

Introduction

Fish are masters of our oceans, rivers, and lakes and are the most conspicuous fauna of these habitats. Many species are also vitally important as food for people around the world. The first fishlike animals known from fossils date back some 480 million years to the Ordovician Period. The earliest fish were jawless, a feature still retained today in hagfish and lampreys. Fish with true jaws (known as acanthodians) did not evolve for another 40-50 million years. It is from such fish that modern-day fish have arisen, although many have gone extinct along the way, including the acanthodians themselves.

Today there are over 26,700 species of fish. They range in size from the tiny dwarf pygmy goby *(Pandaka pygmaea)*, which grows to only 0.4 inches (9 mm), to the giant whale shark *(Rhinocodon typus)*, which can reach 59 feet (18 m).

What Makes a Fish?

Strangely no single feature seems to be totally unique to fish (for example, some amphibians have gills, and many reptiles have scales). Rather it is a combination of features that defines a fish, and most species have all or most of the following characteristics:

- A braincase and limb (fin) skeleton consisting of cartilage or bone.
- Fins, usually (but not always) with spines or supporting rays.
- Breathe through outward directed gills covered by a gill cover (operculum), which results in an external slitlike aperture or a series of slits.
- Bodies usually (but not always) covered in scales.
- A swim bladder used in buoyancy (exceptions include sharks).
- A sensory organ known as the lateral line running in a head to tail direction or another series of sensory pits (as in sharks).
- Cold blooded (poikilothermic)—in other words, the body temperature matches that of the environment (some fish such as tuna can raise their temperature above that of the surrounding water).

1

Rank	Scientific name	Common name
Phylum	Chordata	Animals with a backbone
Superclass	Gnathostomata	Jawed fish
Class	Actinopterygii	Ray-finned fish
Order	Characiformes	Characoids
Family	Characidae	Characins
Genus	*Pygocentrus*	Piranhas
Species	*natereri*	Red-bellied piranha

The kingdom Animalia is subdivided into groups such as classes, families, genera, and species. Above is the classification of the red-bellied piranha.

Fish are adaptable creatures that are found virtually everywhere there is water. The habitats they occupy include the Arctic wastes, fast-flowing mountain streams, slow-flowing rivers, tiny mud pools no larger than an elephant's footprint, crystal-clear warm water reefs, the open sea, the dark cold abysses of the world's oceans where no light reaches, and the water that flows through cave systems.

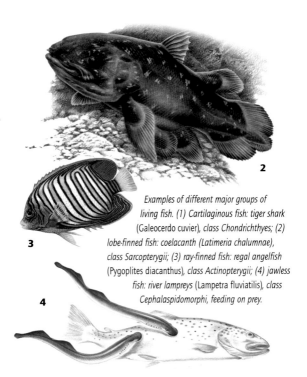

2

Examples of different major groups of living fish. (1) Cartilaginous fish: tiger shark (Galeocerdo cuvier), class Chondrichthyes; (2) lobe-finned fish: coelacanth (Latimeria chalumnae), class Sarcopterygii; (3) ray-finned fish: regal angelfish (Pygoplites diacanthus), class Actinopterygii; (4) jawless fish: river lampreys (Lampetra fluviatilis), class Cephalaspidomorphi, feeding on prey.

3

4

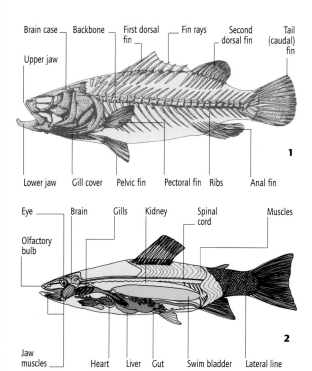

1

Brain case — Backbone — First dorsal fin — Fin rays — Second dorsal fin — Tail (caudal) fin

Upper jaw

Lower jaw — Gill cover — Pelvic fin — Pectoral fin — Ribs — Anal fin

2

Eye — Brain — Gills — Kidney — Spinal cord — Muscles

Olfactory bulb

Jaw muscles — Heart — Liver — Gut — Swim bladder — Lateral line

Naming Fish

Just by looking, we can see that piranhas and perches are probably related, since they look alike, and that eels are quite different from sharks. Scientists take this study much further in the science of taxonomy, in which detailed relationships are worked out using a hierarchy of categories called taxa. The classification (arrangement) of the taxa of fish is particularly complicated, and a full table of hierarchies relevant to this book is given on the following pages. There is much debate among scientists about the classification of fish, and changes occur frequently. The system used here is based on that of Joseph S. Nelson (*Fishes of the World*, John Wiley and Sons, Inc., 1994) with some modifications.

Fish are divided into two broad groups. First, there are the jawless fish in the superclass Agnatha, which contains just 90 or so species in two distinct types—lampreys and hagfish. Second, there are the jawed fish in the superclass Gnathostomata, which contains the remaining species. Jawed fish are subdivided into cartilaginous fish and bony fish. The cartilaginous fish include the sharks and the rays and form the grade Chondrichthiomorphi, with a single class— Chondrichthyes. The bony fish such as eels, piranhas, and perches make up the grade Teleostomi. Beneath these broad categories fish are further divided into other groups (classes, subclasses, divisions, subdivisions, superorders, etc.). The major taxonomic groups with which the lay reader probably identifies are the orders, of which there are about 58. For

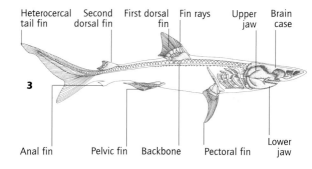

Heterocercal tail fin
Second dorsal fin
First dorsal fin
Fin rays
Upper jaw
Brain case

3

Anal fin
Pelvic fin
Backbone
Pectoral fin
Lower jaw

Typical body plans of major groups of fish, including external features and internal organs. (1) Bony fish skeleton; (2) bony fish internal organs; (3) cartilaginous fish skeleton.

example, all catfish belong to the order Siluriformes. In this book you will find representatives of most fish orders. They are grouped together under headings related to various higher taxa, and are color coded and listed on pages 3 to 5.

Within an order such as Characiformes, all piranhalike fish are placed in the family Characidae along with, for example, tetras. Very closely related piranhas are mostly placed in the genus *Pygocentrus*. Finally, individual piranha species, for example, the red-bellied piranha and the San Francisco piranha, are distinguished by the scientific names *Pygocentrus natteri* and *Pygocentrus piraya* respectively. A classification for the red piranha is shown on page 7.

About this Book

In the *Animal Fact Files: Fish* you will find illustrated articles on 237 species of fish or groups of related fish. Each article follows a fixed structure. The color-coded header strip denotes the group to which each fish belongs, followed by its common name. The fact panel then gives the scientific name of the fish (or group) in question and other taxanomic information. The next section describes different features of the fish and their lifestyles. The artwork illustrates either the species that is the subject of the article or, if the article discusses a group of fish, a representative species. In the latter case a brief caption is also given, often including the size of the species.

The first two articles (Sea Squirts and Salps, Lancelets) deal with groups that, while not fish, are the earliest forms of existing life that share some characteristics with chordates (the major group that includes fish as well as reptiles, amphibians, birds, and mammals).

The survival of many fish, like all animals, is in doubt as they endure and suffer from the pressures brought on them by people. Under the heading "Status," information is given on the threats facing these fish, if any. For definitions of the categories of threat see Glossary under IUCN and CITES.

Groups of Living Fish

SUPERCLASS AGNATHA
(jawless fish)

CLASS CEPHALASPIDOMORPHI

  Order Petromyzontiformes (lampreys)

CLASS MYXINI

  Order Myxiniformes (hagfish)

SUPERCLASS GNATHOSTOMATA
(jawed fish)

GRADE CHONDRICHTHIO-MORPHI

CLASS CHONDRICHTHYES
(cartilaginous fish)

SUBCLASS HOLOCEPHALI

  Order Chimaeriformes (chimaeras)

SUBCLASS ELASMOBRANCHII
(sharks and rays)

SUPERORDER EUSELACHII
  Order Heterodontiformes (bullhead sharks)

  Order Orectolobiformes (carpet sharks)

  Order Carcharhiniformes (ground sharks)

  Order Lamniformes (mackerel sharks)

  Order Hexanchiformes (frilled and cow sharks)

  Order Squaliformes (dogfish sharks)

  Order Squatiniformes (angel sharks)

  Order Pristiophoriformes (saw sharks)

  Order Rajiformes (rays)

GRADE TELEOSTOMI (OSTEICHTHYES) (bony fish)

CLASS SARCOPTERYGII
(lobe-finned fish)

SUBCLASS COELACANTHIMORPHA

  Order Coelacanthiformes (coelacanths)

SUBCLASS POROLEPIFORMES AND DIPNOI (lungfish)

  Order Ceratodontiformes (Australian lungfish)

  Order Lepidosireniformes (South American and African lungfish)

CLASS ACTINOPTERYGII
(ray-finned fish)

SUBCLASS CHONDROSTEI
(cartilaginous bony fish)

  Order Polypteriformes (bichirs and ropefish)

  Order Acipenseriformes (sturgeons and paddlefish)

SUBCLASS NEOPTERYGII ("new fins")

  Order Amiiformes (bowfin)

  Order Semionotiformes (garfish)

DIVISION TELEOSTEI (teleosts)

SUBDIVISION OSTEOGLOSSOMORPHA

  Order Osteoglossiformes (bonytongues and allies)

SUBDIVISION ELOPOMORPHA

  Order Elopiformes (tarpons)

  Order Albuliformes (spiny eels)

  Order Anguilliformes (eels)

  Order Saccopharyngiformes (swallower and gulper eels)

SUBDIVISION CLUPEOMORPHA

  Order Clupeiformes (herrings and allies)

Sea Squirts and Salps

The 6-inch (15-cm) sea vase (*Ciona intestinalis*) is common in docks, harbors, and estuaries in shallow northeast Atlantic waters.

Common name Sea squirts and salps

Classes Ascidiacea (sea squirts), Thaliacea (salps), Larvacea (larvaceans)

Subphylum Urochordata (Tunicata)

Number of species Ascidiacea: about 1,850; Thaliacea: about 70; Larvacea: about 70

Size Individuals from 0.04 in (1 mm) to about 8 in (20 cm) long; colonies up to 40 in (1 m) in sea squirts and over 10 ft (3 m) in salps

Key features Adult sea squirts sedentary, solitary, or colonial; often flask-shaped, sheathed in test or tunic, with gills in hollow center (atrium); no head; inhalant siphon at top of body to take in sea water, exhalant siphon on side to expel water; larval sea squirts tadpolelike, free swimming, and quite different from adults, with chordate characteristics: gill slits, tail behind anus, hollow dorsal nerve cord, and notochord—the forerunner of a backbone; all these features lost on metamorphosis to adult form; in salps both larvae and adults free swimming; adults form colonies in a variety of shapes, e.g., like casks or chains; adult larvaceans solitary, free swimming, and retain some larval characteristics

Breeding Adults hermaphrodite; asexual reproduction involves budding new adults from parent; in sexual reproduction eggs and sperm released into atrium or into open water for fertilization

Diet Food particles filtered from sea water

Habitat Adult Ascidiacea attached to rocks and other organisms on seabed; Thaliacea and Larvacea found in open water

Distribution Worldwide; mostly in shallow oceans and seas, but with some species to 650 ft (200 m)

Status Not threatened

Lancelets

The 4-inch (10-cm) lancelet (*Branchiostoma lanceolatum*) lives in shallow inshore waters in both tropical and temperate regions.

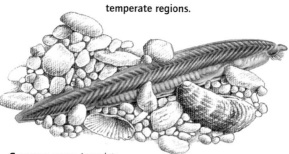

Common name Lancelets

Order Amphioxiformes

Subphylum Cephalochordata (Acrania)

Number of species About 25 in 2 genera: *Branchiostoma* (or *Amphioxus*) and *Epigonichthys*

Size Up to 4 in (10 cm)

Key features Simple, fishlike chordates lacking recognizable head but with hood of tentacles in *Branchiostoma*; have hollow dorsal nerve cord similar to vertebrates, but with notochord instead of vertebrae; body slender and pointed at both ends; distinct muscle blocks in segments; gills well developed; dorsal fin extends from just behind the head to the well-formed tail; a small ventral fin extends from the atriopore to the anus

Breeding Sexes separate; eggs and sperm released into open water where fertilization takes place; free-swimming planktonic tornaria larvae

Diet Filter feeder; water is channeled into the mouth cavity by ring of tentacles around the mouth and then filtered through gill slits in the pharynx (throat); particles are mixed with mucus and move to the intestine to be digested; excess water flows into an area surrounding the pharynx and is discharged through the atriopore

Habitat Inshore shallow water

Distribution Temperate and tropical seas

Status Not threatened

Hagfish and Lampreys

A 24-inch (61-cm) hagfish (*Myxine* species), showing its elongated, eel-like form, simple fin, and mouth tentacles.

Common name Hagfish and lampreys

Classes Myxini (comprising hagfish: order Myxiniformes, family Myxinidae); Cephalaspidomorphi (comprising lampreys: order Petromyzontiformes, family Petromyzontidae)

Superclass Agnatha

Subphylum Vertebrata (Craniata)

Size Up to 46 in (1.2 m) in hagfish; up to 36 in (90 cm) in lampreys

Number of species Hagfish: about 50 in 6 genera; lampreys: about 40 in 7 genera

Key features Lampreys: eel-like with 1 or 2 dorsal fins and simple caudal fin; no biting jaws; mouth a disk with horny teeth; 7 gill openings; ammocete larval stage very different from adult; hagfish: eel-like, white to pale brown, with fleshy median fin and 4–6 tentacles around mouth; no biting jaws

Breeding Lampreys: spawn in rivers and streams, freshwater species moving upstream and marine species entering from sea; some with complex life cycles; hagfish: lay a few large eggs at sea

Diet Lampreys: as larvae, particles filtered from water; parasitic adults attach to host fish and feed on blood and tissues; nonparasitic adults do not feed; hagfish: dead or dying fish and sea mammals on seafloor

Habitat Lampreys: seas and rivers; hagfish: seabed

Distribution Lampreys: temperate marine and freshwater; hagfish: mostly temperate oceans and seas (excluding midocean zones) but also cooler, deeper tropical waters

Status Not threatened

Elephant Fish

Common name Elephant fish (southern beauty, ghost shark)

Scientific name *Callorhynchus milii*

Family Callorhynchidae

Order Chimaeriformes

Size 4 ft (1.2 m)

Key features Two tall triangular dorsal fins present along the back, with a sharp, venomous spine in front of the first dorsal fin; upper lobe of caudal fin is triangular and rather sharklike; very evident protuberance in front of mouth; basic coloration silvery with variable brown markings over body; lives in deep water, coming closer inshore when breeding

Breeding Egg laying; breeds seasonally; eggs relatively large— about 4 in (10 cm) wide and 10 in (25 cm) long; yellowish brown in color; deposited on sandy seabed; young develop slowly in egg cases and begin to hatch from May onward after an interval of 6-8 months; newborn young measure about 4 in (10 cm) long and develop slowly

Diet Invertebrates, mainly different types of shellfish

Habitat Continental shelf; relatively deep water down to 660 ft (200 m); in southern spring they move into shallower areas and are not found below 130 ft (40 m)

Distribution Southern Pacific Ocean around New Zealand, breeding mainly along eastern coast of South Island; sometimes caught off North Island; also encountered off coast of Australia, becoming more common moving south from New South Wales down to Tasmania and South Australia

Status Highly vulnerable because of overfishing

Port Jackson Shark

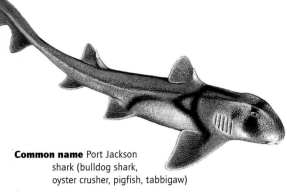

Common name Port Jackson shark (bulldog shark, oyster crusher, pigfish, tabbigaw)

Scientific name *Heterodontus portusjacksoni*

Family Heterodontidae

Order Heterodontiformes

Size Males usually 30 in (76 cm); females 31.5–37.5 in (80–95 cm); maximum length about 5.6 ft (1.7 m)

Key features Blunt headed; pronounced eye ridges originating well in front of eye and running above eye to back of head; underslung mouth with fine, pointed teeth at the front and flat, smoother ones at the back; stout spine in front of the two dorsal fins; large, paddlelike pectoral fins; anal and pelvic fins smaller than pectorals; heterocercal tail

Breeding May migrate up to 500 mi (800 km) to traditional spawning grounds; several males may accompany single female during courtship; mating occurs late winter and spring; internal fertilization; female produces 10–16 leathery eggs (mermaids' purses); females may place egg cases in crevices; embryos obtain nourishment from their egg yolks; eggs hatch after 9–12 months; newborn young measure around 10 in (25.5 cm)

Diet Predominantly mollusks, crustaceans, urchins, starfish, and bony fish

Habitat Predominantly found on rocky substrata, but may also be found over sandy or muddy bottoms; occurs at depths ranging from the intertidal zone down to around 560 ft (170 m)

Distribution From Moreton Bay (north of Brisbane, Australia) southward, westward, and northward to North Island (north of Perth, Western Australia); also around Tasmania; recorded once from New Zealand; doubt surrounds reports of its occurrence at York Sound, Western Australia

Status Not threatened

Nurse Shark

Common name Nurse shark (Atlantic nurse shark)

Scientific name *Ginglymostoma cirratum*

Family Ginglymostomatidae

Order Orectolobiformes

Size Around 14 ft (4.3 m); females slightly larger than males

Key features Body gray above, fading to white on underside; spiracles located behind eyes; distinct forehead slope; short, underslung mouth located well in front of eyes; nostrils and distinct barbels; relatively large dorsal and pectoral fins; caudal fin with long upper lobe held almost in line with body; approachable and generally nonaggressive, but can deliver a powerful bite if provoked

Breeding Several males may accompany a single female, jostling for position; successful male will bite female on the pectoral fin, and she will then roll over; internal fertilization; developing embryos retained until birth; during this time they feed on their yolk sac; 8–28 pups

Diet Mainly bottom-dwelling invertebrates like crabs, lobsters, and octopuses; also bottom-dwelling fish

Habitat Mainly shallow water from around 3 ft (91 cm) down to around 165 ft (50 m); often rests in groups on the bottom during the day, with individuals lying on top of each other

Distribution Eastern Pacific from Baja California to Peru; western Atlantic from Rhode Island south to Brazil; eastern Atlantic—mainly tropical West Africa; one population from western Atlantic migrates to Florida Keys in June each year, gathering in large numbers for courtship and mating

Status Not threatened

Whale Shark

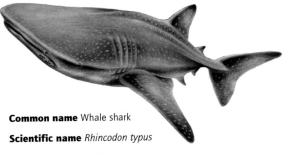

Common name Whale shark

Scientific name *Rhincodon typus*

Family Rhincodontidae

Order Orectolobiformes

Size Around 39 ft (12 m), but may grow to 59 ft (18 m)

Key features Whalelike body with massive, flat head; truncated snout; cavernous mouth with numerous small teeth; body base color grayish with light spots and stripes—the pattern unique to each individual; underside white; 3 distinct ridges along top of body

Breeding Little information available; females may retain fertilized eggs within their bodies until they hatch; up to 300 developing embryos may be held at different stages of development by a single female; newborn whale sharks thought to measure only up to 28 in (71 cm)

Diet Zooplankton, small fish, and other small animals filtered out in vast volumes by the gill rakers

Habitat Both inshore and oceanic waters; found from the surface down to a depth of around 425 ft (130 m)

Distribution Tropical and temperate waters in the Atlantic, Indian, and Pacific Oceans.

Status Listed by IUCN as Vulnerable; legally protected in the Philippines since 1998; the species is particularly vulnerable to exploitation due to its slow rate of reproduction and growth, its highly migratory nature, and low abundance; in recent years dive tourism has developed in a number of locations around the world

Tasseled Wobbegong

Common name
Tasseled wobbegong

Scientific name *Eucrossorhinus dasypogon*

Family Orectolobidae

Order Orectolobiformes

Size Maximum size usually around 4 ft (1.2 m); occasionally reported up to 12 ft (3.7 m)

Key features Flattened body and large, flattened head; numerous ornate skin flaps around the mouth; large mouth located at front of head—not underslung as in most other sharks; body covered in irregular mottled patterns that provide excellent camouflage; fanglike teeth; 2 dorsal fins, approximately equal in size; large pectoral and pelvic fins

Breeding Mating season and duration of pregnancy unknown; number of offspring unknown; embryos obtain nourishment from their yolk sacs during development; may be around 8 in (20 cm) long at birth

Diet Feeds close to the bottom on fish and invertebrates; lies motionless in wait for prey during daylight hours and gulps in any suitable victim that swims within range; during hours of darkness becomes more mobile and actively hunts prey, including crabs, lobsters, squid, octopuses, and fish (even other sharks)

Habitat Shallow, inland waters down to around 130 ft (40 m)

Distribution Western Pacific Ocean, Northern Australia (from Queensland to Western Australia), Indonesia, Papua New Guinea, and Irian Jaya

Status Listed by IUCN as Near Threatened due to coral-reef habitat destruction

Dogfish

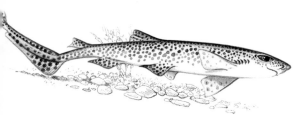

Common name Dogfish (rough hound, lesser-spotted cat shark)

Scientific name *Scyliorhinus canicula*

Family Scyliorhinidae

Order Carcharhiniformes

Size Up to around 3.9 ft (1.2 m), although usually smaller

Key features Slim body and slightly flattened head; body generally light-colored and liberally peppered with dark brown spots; some specimens exhibit lighter spots or dark blotches; large dark eyes; underslung mouth; well-formed pectoral fins, but all other fins—including caudal—relatively small

Breeding During winter months large numbers of females gather close to shore and are joined by males as spring approaches; mating usually occurs later in summer in deeper water, with males entwining their slender bodies around their mates; internal fertilization; females return to shallow water to lay eggs; 18–20 egg cases laid, two at a time; tendrils of egg cases wrap around seaweeds, corals, or any submerged object; incubation 9 months

Diet Mainly bottom-dwelling mollusks (including whelks and clams) and crustaceans (predominantly shrimp and crabs); also bony fish such as seahorses and flatfish, as well as soft-bodied invertebrates like worms and sea cucumbers

Habitat Bottom dwelling; reported at a depth of over 1,300 ft (396 m), but usually at a maximum depth of around 330 ft (100 m), with preferred habitat considerably shallower, including intertidal zone

Distribution Eastern Atlantic from Norway south to the Canary Islands; also Mediterranean

Status Not threatened

Gray Reef Shark

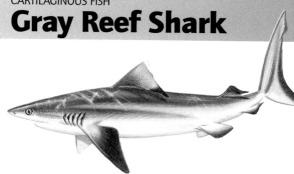

Common name Gray reef shark (long-nosed blacktail shark)

Scientific name *Carcharhinus amblyrhynchos*

Family Carcharhinidae

Order Carcharhiniformes

Size Up to 8.4 ft (2.6 m) but usually smaller

Key features Sleek, dark-gray or bronze-gray back fading to white on the underside; long snout with underslung mouth; caudal fin has distinct black edge (hence one of the shark's common names); some individuals have white-tipped first dorsal fin (they are regarded as *C. wheeleri* by some authorities)

Breeding Internal fertilization; embryos develop a placenta through which they obtain nourishment for up to 1 year; 1–6 pups produced in a litter

Diet Wide range of bony fish, as well as squid, octopuses, lobsters, and crabs

Habitat On continental and island shelves and on coral reefs, preferring deeper waters around the dropoff zone (where the reef plunges sharply at its ocean-facing edge); also found in atoll passes and in shallower areas with strong currents; during the day groups of individuals may rest on the bottom—unlike most sharks, they do not need to swim continuously to force oxygen-rich water to flow over their gills

Distribution Widely distributed in tropical zones of both the Pacific and Indian Oceans; if *C. wheeleri* is accepted as being a variant of *C. amblyrhynchos*, rather than a separate species, then the range extends into the Red Sea and down as far as South Africa

Status Listed by IUCN as Lower Risk near threatened; abundant at many locations within its range, but may be declining in some areas due to fishing; considered of value if protected for dive tourism

Bull Shark

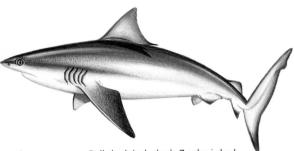

Common name Bull shark (cub shark, Zambezi shark, Lake Nicaragua shark, freshwater whaler, river whaler, Swan River whaler, ground shark)

Scientific name *Carcharhinus leucas*

Family Carcharhinidae

Order Carcharhiniformes

Size Up to 11.5 ft (3.5 m), but usually smaller

Key features Robust-looking, stout body; blunt head with broad snout; saw-edged teeth in upper jaw; small eyes; body uniformly slate-gray color fading to lighter shades on underside; first dorsal fin triangular and much larger than the second; upper lobe of tail much larger than the lower one; bull sharks survive well in captivity and are often seen in public aquaria; capable of cruising speed of approximately 4.3 ft (1.3 m) per second but can generate bursts of 17.4 ft (5.3 m) per second

Breeding Internal fertilization; gestation period of up to a year, during which developing embryos produce a yolk sac placenta; 1–13 pups may be produced in each litter; size at birth: 22–32 in (56–81 cm); pups frequently produced in brackish water, for example, around estuaries

Diet Extensive list of prey, including some unexpected items like hippopotamuses and catfish, plus numerous other animals like turtles, shrimp, lobsters, sea urchins, squid, and octopuses

Habitat Mainly found in shallow inshore areas from the surf zone down to nearly 500 ft (152 m); commonly found in estuaries, large rivers, and some lakes; easily tolerates fresh water and has even been found 2,600 mi (4,200 km) up the Amazon River and in Lake Nicaragua

Distribution All tropical and subtropical regions

Status Listed by IUCN as Lower Risk near threatened

Pyjama Shark

Common name Pyjama shark
(striped cat shark, one-fin
shark)

Scientific name
Poroderma africanum

Family Scyliorhinidae

Order Carcharhiniformes

Size Up to 3.6 ft
(1.1 m); usually
slightly smaller

Key features Long,
slender body; color ash gray overlaid with 7 black stripes
extending from nose to tail; large eyes and spiracles;
mouth barbels relatively short; well-formed pectoral fins;
first dorsal fin much larger than second

Breeding 2 egg cases, each measuring about 3.7 in (9.5 cm)
long, laid every 3 days; incubation around 5.5 months;
each pup measures 5.5–6 in (14–15 cm) long at birth
and weighs around 0.3 oz (8.5 g); young take several
years to reach maturity, and males are slightly smaller
than females by the time they are ready to breed

Diet Wide range of invertebrates—mainly crabs, lobsters,
shrimp, squid, octopuses, and cuttlefish; also bony fish
like hake, gurnard, and anchovy

Habitat From intertidal zone down to depths around 330 ft
(100 m); preferred habitat is rocky shallow inshore
areas with crevices and caves; also found in seagrass meadows

Distribution South African coasts

Status Listed by IUCN as Lower Risk near threatened; lack of
protective legislation, allied to heavy fishing activity
within its geographic and depth range, can result in
unintentional capture of the species; sport fishing adds
to the pressure on some populations; since the species
also has a restricted distribution, concerns for the
pyjama cat shark is beginning to grow

Blotchy Swell Shark

The reticulated swell shark (*Cephaloscyllium fasciatum*) is found in the Indo-West Pacific region in fairly deep water or on or near the borrom.
Length to 15.5 in (40 cm).

Common name Blotchy swell shark

Scientific name *Cephaloscyllium umbratile*

Family Scyliorhinidae (which includes 7 or 8 species in the genus *Cephaloscyllium*, collectively known as swell sharks)

Order Carcharhiniformes

Size Up to 4 feet (1.2 m)

Key features Generally dogfish shaped, but with more rotund, inflatable body; underslung mouth armed with numerous fine, pointed teeth; variable dark blotches on a lighter base color distributed along back, sides, and top surfaces of dorsal and caudal fins; light-colored underside with no blotches or spots; most swell sharks can swallow water or air rapidly in order to inflate their bodies and wedge themselves against cavity walls for safety

Breeding Long breeding season, no clearly demarcated beginning or end; egg cases bearing tendrils laid in pairs; incubation around 12 months; newborn pups measure around 6–8.5 in (15–22 cm)

Diet Mostly bony and cartilaginous fish, including other sharks, skates, rays, sardines, mackerel, flatfish, and other bottom-dwelling or slow-moving species; also octopuses and squid

Habitat Mainly on rocky substrata ranging from around 65 ft (20 m) to 655 ft (200 m) deep

Distribution Western Pacific Ocean from around Japan to the South China Sea; may also occur around Papua New Guinea and Irian Jaya

Status Not threatened

Tiger Shark

Common name
Tiger shark

Scientific name *Galeocerdo cuvier*

Family Carcharhinidae

Order Carcharhiniformes

Size Commonly attains a length of 10–14 ft (3–4.3 m) and weighs between 850–1,400 lb (385–635 kg); maximum length reported 24.3 ft (7.4 m) and a weight of over 6,855 lb (3,110 kg)

Key features Snout broad and blunt; large mouth with large serrated (cock's comb) teeth; grayish body with darker vertical bars forming "tiger" pattern; patterning particularly well pronounced in juveniles, but fading with age; white underside; top lobe of caudal fin long and powerful

Breeding Livebearing species in which litter sizes vary between 11 and 82 pups; gestation up to 12–13 months; newborn pups measure 20–40 in (51–102 cm)

Diet Extremely varied—virtually anything edible; also swallows an array of nonedible items, including bottles, cans, pieces of metal, rubber tires, money, cloth, sacks of coal, and even explosives; species sometimes described as the ocean's "dustbin with fins"; attacks and saws chunks off prey from very first bite (instead of biting and then releasing), not allowing victim a chance to escape; consequently responsible for more human fatalities than the great white shark

Habitat From intertidal zone down to depths of around 460 ft (140 m); reported as being able to descend to around 1,000 ft (305 m) or deeper; usually found near the surface and frequently in river estuaries and lagoons; may be found in the open ocean but is not a true oceanic species

Distribution Widely distributed in most tropical and warm-temperate regions, but not found in the Mediterranean

Status Listed by IUCN as Lower Risk near threatened due to declines of several populations where heavily fished

Whitetip Reef Shark

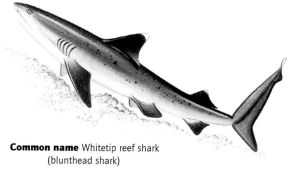

Common name Whitetip reef shark
(blunthead shark)

Scientific name *Triaenodon obesus*

Family Carcharhinidae

Order Carcharhiniformes

Size Up to 7 ft (2.1 m), but often smaller

Key features Blunt nose; underslung mouth; brownish-gray
coloration on back, fading to white on the underside;
some specimens have dark spots or blotches; distinct
white tips on the first dorsal fin and the upper lobe of
the caudal fin; pointed pectoral fins; long upper lobe on
the caudal fin

Breeding Groups of males may follow single female; mating
includes characteristic biting of the female and grasping
of her pectoral fin in order to secure the appropriate
position for sperm transfer; mating may last up to 3
minutes; gestation period may last just over 5 months
(although periods exceeding 1 year have been reported);
1–5 pups produced in each brood; 20–24 in (51–61 cm)
at birth; maturity takes at least 5 years

Diet Large selection of bony fish; also invertebrates such as
lobsters, crabs, squid, and octopuses

Habitat Shallow waters around reefs (down to depths of
around 130 ft /40 m); selects crevices, caves, and
overhangs as daytime resting places; also frequents
reef flats and lagoons

Distribution Widely distributed in most tropical regions of the
Indian Ocean; also west, central, and eastern Pacific and
Oceania, including Queensland, northern and western
Australia, Hawaii, Cocos Islands, Galápagos, Panama,
and Costa Rica

Status Listed by IUCN as Lower Risk near threatened due to
fishing pressures

Hammerheads

The great hammerhead (*Sphyrna mokarran*) has been known to attack humans.
Length to 20 feet (6.1 m).

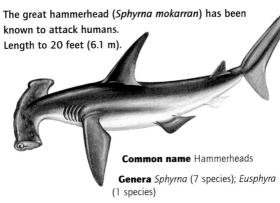

Common name Hammerheads

Genera *Sphyrna* (7 species); *Eusphyra* (1 species)

Family Carcharhinidae (sometimes placed in their own family, Sphyrnidae)

Order Carcharhiniformes

Size Smallest: scalloped hammerhead (*S. lewini*)—3 feet (90 cm); largest: great hammerhead (*S. mokarran*)—around 19.7 ft (6 m)

Key features Characteristic and variable lateral lobes on head (the "hammer"); eyes at ends of "hammer"; nostrils widely spaced near outer front extremities of "hammer"; body powerfully muscled; first dorsal fin high and prominent, second very small; pectoral fins small; caudal fin with long, pointed upper lobe bearing a distinct notch, lower lobe small and pointed

Breeding Internal fertilization: nourishment initially supplied by egg yolk; subsequent nourishment via placenta; gestation around 8 months; litter sizes from 6 to over 40 pups, depending on species and size of female

Diet Wide range of prey from open-water and bottom-dwelling bony fish to skates, rays, other sharks (including hammerheads), squid, crustaceans, and sea snakes

Habitat Open and shallow waters, ranging in depth from inshore reefs and near-shore shallows down to around 1,000 ft (300 m) in scalloped hammerhead; most species stay in upper 260 ft (80 m) of the water column

Distribution Widespread in many tropical and warm-temperate regions

Status IUCN lists at various levels of threat: slender hammerhead (*E. blochii*)—Near Threatened; crown shark (*S. corona*)—Near Threatened; scalloped hammerhead (*S. lewini*)—Lower Risk near threatened; great hammerhead (*S. mokarran*)—Data Deficient; smooth hammerhead (*S. zygaena*)—Lower Risk near threatened; some populations have declined due to uncontrolled fishing

Megamouth Shark

Common name Megamouth shark

Scientific name *Megachasma pelagios*

Family Megachasmidae

Order Lamniformes

Size Largest female known measured 16.9 ft (5.2 m); males probably smaller

Key features Large, bulbous head with short snout; huge mouth with numerous very small teeth; lining of the mouth silvery; tapering body; upper lobe of caudal fin about 1.5 times the length of the lower lobe; body color blackish-brown above; lower half brilliant white; tips of pectoral and pelvic fins white; posterior edges of pectoral, pelvic, dorsal, and anal fins also white

Breeding Fertilization internal; mating in southern California waters may occur in October/November, but not known for certain; no details for other regions; embryos may consume unfertilized eggs during development, but number of pups produced, duration of their period of development, or frequency of broods produced by a female all unknown

Diet Predominantly euphausiid (luminescent deepwater) shrimp, some jellyfish, and other invertebrates

Habitat Midwater (pelagic) zones of the open ocean—hence its specific name, *pelagios*; known to migrate daily from depths of 40 ft (12.1 m) or less to around 545 ft (166 m), but may dive to around 3,300 ft (1,000 m)

Distribution Recorded in Atlantic, Indian, and Pacific Oceans; first caught in 1976 but not described and formally identified as a new species until 1983

Status Listed by IUCN as Data Deficient; world population unknown

Basking Shark

Common name Basking shark (sunfish)

Scientific name *Cetorhinus maximus*

Family Cetorhinidae

Order Lamniformes

Size Around 33 ft (10 m), but possibly up to 50.5 ft (15.4 m)

Key features Variable color—brown, dusky black, or blue along the back, becoming lighter toward dull white belly; snout pointed; mouth cavernous; skin covered in small denticles and thick layer of foul-smelling mucus; 5 large gill slits, inside which is the food-filtering mechanism consisting of gill rakers; caudal fin typically sharklike, with upper lobe longer than lower

Breeding Internal fertilization followed by a gestation period of around 3.5 years; developing embryos believed to feed on unfertilized eggs during gestation; females thought to give birth to 1 or 2 pups measuring about 5.5 ft (1.7 m) in length (although some estimates indicate up to 50 young in a single batch)

Diet Planktonic invertebrates filtered from water by the gill rakers

Habitat Spotted mainly in inshore and offshore surface waters, but suspected of also inhabiting deeper zones, possibly down to 650 ft (198 m) or more

Distribution Temperate regions of Pacific and Atlantic Oceans, extending—along western coast of American continent—from British Columbia to Baja California; on east coast ranges from Newfoundland to South America, perhaps avoiding Caribbean; in eastern Atlantic ranges from Scandinavia to southern Africa; also found in Mediterranean and Black Sea, eastern Indian Ocean, around Australia, New Zealand, and up to Asian coasts, past Japan and northward

Status Listed by IUCN as Vulnerable for the species overall, but Endangered for the north Pacific and northeast Atlantic population; not listed by CITES

Thresher Sharks

The common thresher (*Alopias vulpinus*) is the largest of the three species, growing to 20 feet (6.1 m) and is found throughout the world from temperate to tropical seas.

Common name
Thresher sharks

Genus *Alopias*

Family Alopiidae

Order Lamniformes

Number of species 3

Size Up to 20 ft (6.1 m) depending on species

Key features Strong, muscular cylindrical body; upper lobe of tail hugely extended and approximately as long as body, lower lobe very small by comparison; first dorsal fin large in comparison to the second; pectoral fins large and sickle-shaped; body color gray, purplish-gray to black on top, depending on species and on individual; belly white to creamy white

Breeding Very small broods of 2–7 pups produced; during development they feed on unfertilized eggs; duration of gestation unknown

Diet Mainly midwater fish, squid, and crustaceans

Habitat Open surface waters preferred, but may also be found in deeper water and close to shore—the latter particularly during juvenile phase; the common thresher (*A. vulpinus*) has been recorded at depths of 1,200 ft (365 m), the bigeye thresher (*A. superciliosus)* at 1,640 ft (500 m), and the pelagic, or smalltooth, thresher (*A. pelagicus*) at 500 ft (152 m)

Distribution Widely distributed in tropical and temperate regions

Status Listed by IUCN as Data Deficient; world population unknown, but diminishing in some coastal areas as a result of hunting for their fins and meat

Great White Shark

Common name Great white shark (white pointer, blue pointer, maneater, Tommy, death shark, uptail, white death)

Scientific name *Carcharodon carcharias*

Family Lamnidae

Order Lamniformes

Size Specimens in excess of 36 ft (11 m) reported, but confirmed data indicates a maximum size of 18–20 ft (5.5–6.0m)

Key features Torpedo-shaped body with conical, pointed snout; teeth of upper and lower jaws very similar and saw-edged—upper teeth slightly broader; top half of body slate-gray to brownish; irregular line separates top half from pure-white lower half of body; lobes of caudal fin more similar to each other than in most other species, but upper lobe a little larger than lower; underside of pectoral fins have blackish tips

Breeding Livebearing species that gives birth to 5–14 young (probably more) after gestation period of up to a year; scars predominantly on pectoral fins of mature great white females suggest males bite females during mating, as in other sharks

Diet Mainly bony fish; also cartilaginous fish (including other sharks), turtles, seabirds, and marine mammals, including dolphins, seals, and sea lions

Habitat Wide range of habitats from surfline to offshore (but rarely midocean) and from surface down to around depths exceeding 820 ft (250 m)—although it has been reported to dive to a depth of over 4,000 ft (over 1,200 m)

Distribution Predominantly in warm-temperate and subtropical waters, but also warmer areas

Status Listed by IUCN as Vulnerable; world population sometimes quoted at around 10,000, but true numbers unknown

Goblin Shark

Common name Goblin shark (elfin shark)

Scientific name *Mitsukurina owstoni*

Family Mitsukurinidae

Order Lamniformes

Size Largest-known specimen to date, a male, measured 12.6 ft (3.7 m); females are generally larger, so this is not likely to be the maximum size for the species

Key features Most striking feature is the bladelike snout richly supplied with sensory cells; mouth armed with numerous, widely separated fanglike teeth; jaw can be extended; eyes small and reflective; somewhat flabby body pinkish-white to gray; caudal fin long and slender with no lower lobe

Breeding No details known, but believed to produce live young that feed on unfertilized eggs during development

Diet Poorly known, but includes fish, squid, octopuses, and crustaceans; prey probably detected by sensory cells in the snout

Habitat Believed to be a midwater species with a depth range of 130–4,265 ft (40–1,300 m)

Distribution Patchy but widespread distribution, including Japan, New Zealand, Australia, South Africa, Portugal, Madeira, western Indian Ocean, and Pacific Ocean

Status Listed by IUCN as Least Concern; world population unknown, but may not be as rare as once thought; small-scale commercial fishing exists in Japan

Black Dogfish

The bareskin dogfish (*Centroscyllium kamoharai*) grows to 23.5 inches (60 cm) or more. It often looks ragged or bare when caught because the dermal denticles rub off easily. It lives at depths from 2,395 feet (730 m) to 3,937 feet (1,200 m) in the western Pacific.

Common name Black dogfish

Genus *Centroscyllium*

Family Dalatiidae (classified as family Etmopteridae by some authorities)

Order Squaliformes

Number of species 7

Size Largest species (black dogfish, *C. fabricii*) grows to 41 in (107 cm); smallest species (ornate dogfish, *C. ornatum*) known to attain a length of 12 in (30 cm)

Key features Slender body; teeth comblike in all species; coloration ranges from grayish to black and chocolate-brown—combtooth dogfish (*C. nigrum*) is stippled black with white fin tips; all possess luminous organs; bareskin dogfish (*C. kamoharai*) has few denticles (toothlike scales) on the skin; both dorsal fins have grooved spines in all species, with the second being larger than the first

Breeding Details only available for black dogfish; size of litter and duration of gestation period unknown, but pups are 5.5 in (14 cm) long at birth; nourishment during development is derived entirely from egg yolk

Diet Details not available for most species; those that are available reveal that small fish, crustaceans, squid, and jellyfish form part of the diet; may hunt in groups in order to overcome prey larger than themselves

Habitat Deep waters down to 5,250 ft (1,600 m) depending on species; at least 1 species—black dogfish—may be found in relatively shallow water (590 ft/180 m)

Distribution Parts of Atlantic, Indian, and Pacific Oceans

Status Listed by IUCN as Data Deficient; world population unknown but probably being reduced by incidental catch in deepwater fisheries

Greenland Shark

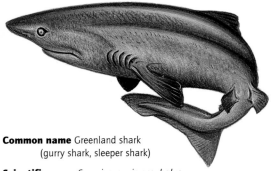

Common name Greenland shark
(gurry shark, sleeper shark)

Scientific name *Somniosus microcephalus*

Family Dalatiidae (classified as family Somniosidae by some
authorities)

Order Squaliformes

Size Around 21 ft (6.4 m); lengths greater than 23 ft (7 m)
also reported

Key features Snout blunt with underslung mouth; long pointed
teeth in the upper jaw and broader cutting teeth in
the lower jaw; eyes usually with one large parasitic,
luminous copepod attached to each; body color
ranges from pinkish through gray to black; like all
dogfish sharks, this species lacks an anal fin; dorsal
fin spines are also lacking; caudal fin has well-developed
lower lobe

Breeding Very little is known; reproduction involves nonplacental
development of embryos; around 10 pups are reported
in a brood, measuring 15 in (38 cm) at birth

Diet Mainly preys on fish and pinnipeds (seals and sea lions),
but scavenges on a wide range of species, including
terrestrial mammals that drown and sink to the bottom

Habitat From the surface down to nearly 7,220 ft (2,200 m);
may also be found around river mouths and in bays

Distribution Northern Atlantic and Arctic Oceans

Status Not threatened; although the flesh of the Greenland
shark is thought to be toxic, Canadian Inuit hunt the
shark and repeatedly boil the meat to kill the toxins;
they also use its tough skin as leather and teeth from
the lower jaw as hair-cutting knives

Frilled Shark

Common name Frilled shark (frill shark, frilled-gilled shark, eel shark, collared shark)

Scientific name *Chlamydoselachus anguineus*

Family Chlamydoselachidae

Order Hexanchiformes

Size Fully mature females up to 6.6 ft (2 m); males about 5 ft (1.5 m)

Key features Head bears terminally located mouth (i.e., at tip of snout rather than under it); 6 gill slits, all with frilled edges; first pair of gill flaps join in the throat area; numerous three-pointed teeth arranged in 25–27 rows; long, eel-like body; folds of skin run lengthwise along the underside of the body; lateral line organ not fully enclosed; body coloration dark brown to gray; all fins, except pectorals, set well down body; caudal fin has long upper lobe and very small lower lobe; 1 dorsal fin

Breeding No distinct breeding season; following fertilization, eggs are retained within female's body, and developing embryos nourished by rich yolk supply; 2–12 pups (average 6) produced after a gestation usually reported to last 1–2 years, but which may last up to 3.5 years; pups measure up to 24 in (61 cm) at birth; males attain maturity when around 3.9 ft (1.2 m) long, females when between 4.6–4.9 ft (1.4–1.5 m) long

Diet Predominantly squid and bony fish

Habitat Deep waters down to 4,200 ft (1,280 m), but may also be found at shallower depths of around 390–400 ft (120 m)

Distribution Specimens have been collected in numerous geographical locations, from Norway to Madeira, around Japan, South Africa, Australia, and west coast of the U.S.

Status Listed by IUCN as Near Threatened; concern at reduced population due to incidental catch in deep-sea fisheries

Bluntnose Sixgill Shark

Common name Bluntnose sixgill shark

Scientific name *Hexanchus griseus*

Family Hexanchidae

Order Hexanchiformes

Size Females up to 15.8 ft (4.8 m); males smaller

Key features Typically blunt head with underslung mouth; upper jaw teeth sawlike, lower jaw teeth pointed; stout body; six gill openings; single dorsal fin set well back near the caudal fin; caudal has long upper lobe and short lower one

Breeding As many as 108 pups may be produced in a single litter; pups measure around 28 in (70 cm) at birth; nourishment consists of the rich supply of yolk that the eggs contain; gestation may take 1–2 years or longer; some populations may breed in shallow water

Diet Wide ranging, including numerous species of bony fish such as marlin, angler fish, hagfish, other sharks, and rays; also whale carcasses, pinnipeds (seals and sea lions), plus crustaceans

Habitat Found from the intertidal zone—but only under certain conditions—down to 6,150 ft (1,875 m); top end of usual depth range around 300 ft (90 m); during July to November bluntnose sixgill sharks move into shallow water in a few locations off British Columbia, Canada; although extremely sensitive to light, they can withstand the shallow-water conditions because dense plankton blooms that occur at that time of year filter much of the light

Distribution Wide-ranging distribution in most tropical and temperate zones

Status Listed by IUCN as Lower Risk near threatened due to fishery activities

Common Angel Shark

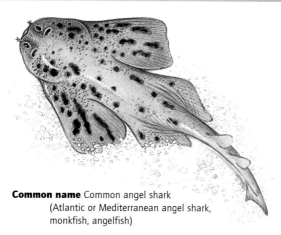

Common name Common angel shark (Atlantic or Mediterranean angel shark, monkfish, angelfish)

Scientific name *Squatina squatina*

Family Squatinidae

Order Squatiniformes

Size Up to 8 ft (2.4 m) reported, but usually smaller

Key features Mouth located close to tip of snout; eyes on top of head; large spiracles behind the eyes; very flat body; ventrally placed gills; body color mottled grayish, greenish, or brownish; light-colored underside; pectorals large and winglike; pelvics smaller but still winglike; both sets of fins held close to the body; small thorns present on the snout and above the eyes; may also have thorns as far as the dorsal fins

Breeding Birth occurs in summer in the northern parts of the range and winter in the south; gestation lasts about 10 months; 7–25 pups measuring 8–12 in (20–30 cm) produced per litter

Diet Mainly bottom-dwelling fish like flatfish, rays, and skates; also invertebrates, including crabs, lobsters, and squid

Habitat Mainly found on sandy and muddy bottoms, often with body buried and eyes showing above the surface

Distribution From eastern North Atlantic (including Norway, Sweden, and Shetland Islands) southward to northern Morocco and West Sahara (taking in the Canary Islands); also in the Mediterranean

Status Listed by IUCN as Vulnerable as bycatch in fisheries

Longnose Saw Shark

Common name Longnose saw shark (common saw shark, little saw shark)

Scientific name *Pristiophorus cirratus*

Family Pristiophoridae

Order Pristiophoriformes

Size Up to 54 in (137 cm)

Key features Long rostrum (snout or saw) with large pointed teeth separated by one to several smaller pointed teeth; two long barbels on underside of saw; head somewhat flattened, particularly the front half; long, slender body; body color brown or grayish-brown on top, with large, darker blotches; white underside; well-formed fins, but no anal fin

Breeding Females may breed every year or every other year; gestation period lasts about a year; 3–22 pups may be produced in a litter; nourishment during gestation derived from egg yolk; pups 11–14.5 in (28–37 cm) at birth

Diet Predominantly small fish, squid, and crustaceans

Habitat Sandy or muddy bottom preferred, mainly on the continental shelf and slope, but may also enter shallower waters and brackish habitats; depth range from around 130–1,020 ft (40–310 m)

Distribution Southern Australian waters from Western Australia along the south coast to New South Wales; also found around Tasmania; reports from elsewhere may not be accurate

Status Listed by IUCN as Least Concern; its range overlaps that of several commercial fisheries in the region, and it is caught in considerable numbers; however, no data currently available to assess effect on overall population

Great-Tooth Sawfish

Common name Great-tooth sawfish (southern sawfish, freshwater sawfish)

Scientific name *Pristis microdon*

Family Pristidae

Order Rajiformes

Size Overall body length recorded up to 46 ft (14 m)

Key features Flat, narrow snout with well-spaced teeth of matching size around its edges, creating an impression of a saw; evident dorsal and caudal fins; first dorsal fin positioned in front of pelvic fins on sides of body; 14–22 pairs of large teeth on each side; swims like a shark; solitary

Breeding Female gives birth to litters of often more than 20 young; breeding period coincides with the rainy season in parts of its range (November to December in northern Queensland); may not breed for the first time until more than 15 years old

Diet Mainly fish; some invertebrates

Habitat Shallow areas of the sea; can also be encountered in estuaries and rivers

Distribution From Africa through the tropical Indo-Pacific region to southeast Asia, north to the Philippines, and south to Australia

Status Listed by IUCN as Endangered; numbers have fallen significantly in recent years as a result of overfishing; heavily hunted as a source of food and for the saws, which are sold as curios; habitat changes, pollution, and relatively low reproductive rate have also contributed to population declines

Marbled Ray

Common name Marbled ray (spotted torpedo)

Scientific name *Torpedo marmorata*

Family Torpedinidae

Order Rajiformes

Size Up to 40 in (1 m) in diameter

Key features Large, round disk shape; nostrils and mouth on underside of body; short tail with clearly divided caudal fin; 2 dorsal fins, the first shorter than the second; variable marbled appearance; nocturnal by nature; uses its electrical discharge to capture prey; the shock from a marbled ray can stun a human badly enough to make him or her drown, although the voltage will not kill directly

Breeding Viviparous, producing 5–32 pups after long gestation period of about 1 year; female only gives birth once every 3 years and cannot conceive again for 2 years after producing pups; young marbled rays measure about 4 in (10 cm) long at birth

Diet Small, bottom-dwelling fish and crustaceans; prey is seized and paralyzed with powerful electrical charge; may choke to death on large prey when swallowing, since it can catch victims larger than itself

Habitat Shallow areas of sea grass and on reefs

Distribution From northern waters around the British Isles to the Mediterranean Sea and south as far as the Cape of Good Hope, South Africa

Status Not threatened

Thornback Ray

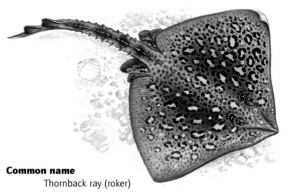

Common name
Thornback ray (roker)

Scientific name *Raja clavata*

Family Rajidae

Order Rajiformes

Size 4 ft (1.2 m)

Key features Short snout with rounded tip, the disk wider than the body; very variable brown coloration on upper body, also blotched with both light and darker markings, may even have a marbled appearance; covered in prickles; undersurface of body is white; tail barred

Breeding During mating male holds female with his claspers and the pair wrap their bodies around each other; female lays up to 20 eggs every day from March to August; oblong eggs up to 3.5 in (9 cm) long and almost 2.75 in (7 cm) in diameter; young thornbacks emerge after about 5 months

Diet Mainly crustaceans; also fish

Habitat Sandy areas, largely on coastal shelf; lives near seabed

Distribution Eastern Atlantic ranging from Iceland and Norway down through the North Sea as far south as Namibia in southwestern Africa, possibly even down to South Africa; also ranges through Mediterranean to Black Sea

Status Listed by IUCN as Lower Risk near threatened; relatively common but heavily fished in places, with some restrictions on catches

Blue Skate

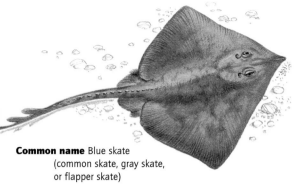

Common name Blue skate
(common skate, gray skate,
or flapper skate)

Scientific name *Dipturus batis* (*Raja batis*)

Family Rajidae

Order Rajiformes

Size 9.4 ft (2.85 m)

Key features Large, with long snout; dark olive-gray to brown
with numerous pale whitish spots on upper surface of
body; underside of body white, with dark spotting,
especially pronounced in young fish and males, creating
a bluish-gray appearance; protective layer of up to 18
thorns runs down the tail; males have more pronounced
spines over the snout and on the back

Breeding Mating occurs in spring; male holds female with his
claspers; fertilization internal; female lays 1 or 2 eggs
during the summer; large eggs measure about 5.5 in
(14 cm) x 10 in (25 cm); young skates hatch about 6
months later and resemble miniature adults (although
thorns develop later)

Diet Crustaceans, some flatfish

Habitat Coastal zone to 2,000 ft (600 m); lives near the seabed

Distribution Eastern Atlantic, ranging from Iceland and
northern parts of Norway down to Adriatic and
Mediterranean, extending as far south as Senegal coast

Status Listed by IUCN as Endangered in many areas due to
heavy fishing

Common Guitarfish

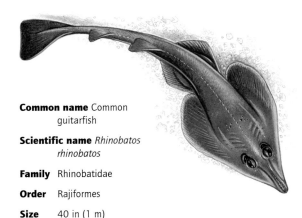

Common name Common guitarfish

Scientific name *Rhinobatos rhinobatos*

Family Rhinobatidae

Order Rajiformes

Size 40 in (1 m)

Key features Large head with variable range of enlarged, thornlike denticles running down the midline; elongated body; narrow tail; brown on upperparts, white below; swims over the bottom using powerful tail action, sometimes buries into soft mud or sand

Breeding Females give birth to litters of up to 10 young, sometimes twice a year; fingerlike projections (villi) in the female's uterus produce nutrient-rich secretion known as "uterine milk" that sustains the young fish during development

Diet Mainly invertebrates rather than fish; uses its head and pectoral fins to trap prey on the seabed; secures victim with pectoral fins as it directs it toward the mouth; pattern of dentition is such that it can easily crush hard shells of crustaceans (even mussels) and extract flesh

Habitat Relatively shallow coastal waters

Distribution Found in eastern Atlantic Ocean ranging from the southern part of the Bay of Biscay off the coast of Spain into the Mediterranean region, south as far as Angola

Status Not threatened but persecuted for damage to shellfish stocks in some areas; not intensively fished

Common Stingray

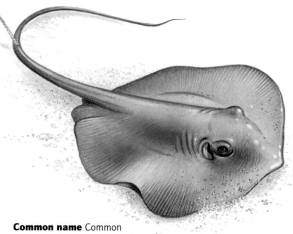

Common name Common
    stingray

Scientific name *Dasyatis pastinaca*

Family Dasyatidae

Order Rajiformes

Size 2 ft (60 cm)

Key features Relatively broad, triangular front to body; long,
    narrow tail twice as long as distance between snout and
    vent; dark color on upper surface, light below; prominent
    spiracles adjacent to eyes; sharp sting resembling a
    dagger, measuring up to 14 in (35 cm) long, projects
    backward from rear portion of tail; sting used for
    defensive purposes (rather than to capture prey) and
    delivers neurotoxic venom

Breeding Eggs retained in female's body; she gives birth to
    6–9 young after gestation period of about 4 months,
    during which young are nourished by outgrowths from
    her uterus

Diet Invertebrates and fish

Habitat Open areas of seabed close to shore; stays close to
    sandy bottom

Distribution Northeastern Atlantic down to Mediterranean,
    most common in the west; recorded as far south as
    coast of Zaire

Status Not threatened; still relatively common but potentially
    vulnerable, especially where heavily fished; however,
    5 other species of *Dasyatis* listed under various
    categories of threat by the IUCN

Ocellate River Stingray

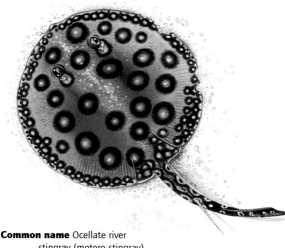

Common name Ocellate river stingray (motoro stingray)

Scientific name *Potamotrygon motoro*

Family Potamotrygonidae

Order Rajiformes

Size 40 in (1 m)

Key features Attractive ringed markings on body, which is quite brightly colored compared with background coloration of the upper parts; skin relatively smooth; a row of sharp thorns runs down the middle of the narrow tail; a deadly stinging spine present near the tip of tail

Breeding Mating occurs mainly in September and October; female gives birth to live young after gestation period of about 5 months; developing young nourished first by yolk of the egg and later by secretions from mother's uterus

Diet Fish and invertebrates

Habitat Lives entirely in fresh water; found in relatively clear areas where bottom is sandy or muddy

Distribution Various river systems in South America, including Amazon and Orinoco, ranging south to Uruguay and Paraguay

Status Along with 4 other species of *Potamotrygon* listed by IUCN as Data Deficient, so numbers may be declining

Round Stingray

Common name Round stingray (Haller's round ray)

Scientific name *Urobatis halleri*

Family Urolophidae

Order Rajiformes

Size 22 in (56 cm)

Key features Rounded disk, smooth appearance; light brown coloration with slight yellowish markings; paler on underparts; tail short with a long, thick, serrated spine on the upper surface; ends in a prominent, leaf-shaped caudal fin; female usually grows slightly larger than male

Breeding Breeding triggered by rise in sea temperature; male nibbles at female's disk as prelude to mating, which takes place with male inverted beneath female's body; female gives birth to up to 6 live young after gestation period of about 3 months; prolific species, with nearly all mature females giving birth every year, some twice a year (having unusual ability to store sperm from previous mating for second brood); young measure about 3 in (7.5 cm) across at birth; they grow fast and can breed at 31 months old

Diet Sand worms, crustaceans, and bivalves

Habitat Sandy areas of coastline; ranges close to shore

Distribution Eastern North Pacific ranging from Humboldt Bay in northern California south to Panama in Central America

Status Not threatened; relatively numerous

Spotted Eagle Ray

Common name Spotted eagle ray

Scientific name *Aetobatus narinari*

Family Myliobatidae

Order Myliobatiformes

Size 6 ft (1.8 m), sometimes even larger

Key features Obviously and relatively even whitish or bluish-white spotted patterning over the dark slatey to chestnut-brown upper surface of the body; underparts predominantly white, extending onto the sides of the face; broad, projecting lower jaw; long, narrow tail up to 3 times the length of body, with inconspicuous stinging spines near the base; active and social by nature

Breeding Receptive female usually mates with several males; mating takes form of embracing each other on underparts to avoid damage by spines; female gives birth to 4 live young after gestation period of about 1 year; young nourished during development by food produced through outgrowths from mother's uterus

Diet Mainly clams, oysters, and crustaceans; digs up prey buried in seabed with spadelike snout; breaks open shells with little effort due to flattened, platelike structure of teeth

Habitat Sandy areas relatively near the coast

Distribution Very extensive, found in temperate and tropical areas of the Atlantic off the coasts of both the Americas, Europe, and Africa; also ranges from the Red Sea into the Indian and Pacific Oceans

Status Listed by IUCN as Data Deficient with no detailed information on populations, although taken as bycatch in fisheries around the world

Manta Ray

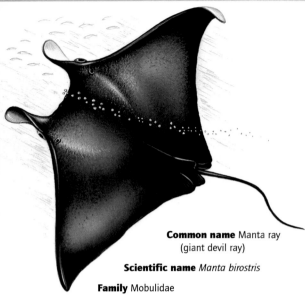

Common name Manta ray
(giant devil ray)

Scientific name *Manta birostris*

Family Mobulidae

Order Myliobatiformes

Size 17 ft (5.2 m); Atlantic mantas are largest

Key features Very distinctive horn-shaped projections (cephalic
fins) extend down beneath the eyes; blackish-brown on
dorsal surface, with a variable white collar whose
patterning allows individuals to be identified; whitish on
ventral side of body; active by nature, swimming over
long distances rather than concealing itself on seabed

Breeding Female gives birth to a single young after gestation
period of about 13 months; young well developed at
birth, with a wingspan of over 3 ft (1 m)

Diet Typically feeds on plankton; sometimes small fish

Habitat Usually in upper reaches of the ocean; sometimes found
in estuaries and even in rivers

Distribution Circumglobal in tropical parts of Atlantic,
Indian, and Pacific Oceans; ranges as far south as
Brazil, sometimes as far north as New England and
Georges Bank on eastern U.S. seaboard, although
not consistently recorded north of the Carolinas;
occurs northward to Redondo Beach, California, on
Pacific Coast

Status Listed by IUCN as Data Deficient; some populations
have declined due to fisheries; now very scarce in
Gulf of California

Japanese Devil Ray

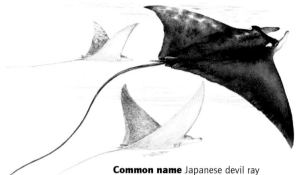

Common name Japanese devil ray
(spinetail mobula)

Scientific name *Mobula japanica*

Family Mobulidae

Order Myliobatiformes

Size 4 ft (1.2 m) long

Key features Color varies from black to blue on dorsal surface,
with large dark blotches on white underparts; young are
discernible by their pure white underparts as well as
white, crescent-shaped markings near the shoulders
above the pectoral fins; mouth positioned ventrally, set
some distance back from the leading edge of the disk
itself; slender tail is about twice as long as body, with a
venomous spine at its base; small, triangular-shaped
dorsal fin

Breeding Mating occurs during summer; during mating, female
swims on her back beneath male, who holds on with his
claspers; female gives birth to a single pup after
gestation period of about 1 year; during development
pup is nourished first by yolk and then by food produced
through outgrowths in the mother's uterus; young
relatively large and well developed at birth, with a disk
measuring about 33 in (85 cm) in diameter

Diet Mainly plankton filtered from sea water

Habitat Relatively shallow coastal waters; typically lives close
to surface; active and migratory by nature

Distribution Unclear but suspected of having a circumglobal
range, although best known from the Pacific region,
especially the eastern Pacific, extending from the
central California coast down to Peru; also quite
common in other localities in the region, including
Japan and Hawaii

Status Listed by IUCN as Near Threatened, in particular due to
gillnet fisheries for tuna in Indonesia; some populations
approaching Vulnerable

Coelacanth

Common name Coelacanth

Scientific names *Latimeria chalumnae, L. menadoensis*

Family Latimeriidae

Order Coelacanthiformes

Number of species 2 known

Size Up to 6 ft (1.8 m) long and weighing up to 210 lb (95 kg)

Form Bluish base color when alive, with light pinkish-white blotches

Breeding Livebearer; a few large eggs, each about 3.5 in (9 cm) in diameter and weighing 10.6–12.4 oz (300–350 g), are released into the oviduct, which acts as a womb for embryos that grow to at least 12 in (30 cm) before birth

Diet Smaller fish

Habitat Cold waters in deep ocean down to more than 330 ft (100 m)

Distribution Cape Province and KwaZulu-Natal (South Africa); Comoro Archipelago (islands between northern tip of Madagascar and east coast of Africa); a related species, *Latimeria menadoensis*, is known from northern Sulawesi, Indonesia

Status Listed by IUCN as Critical with little idea of population; CITES: Appendix I

Lungfish

The Australian lungfish (*Neoceratodus forsteri*) grows to a length of up to 5 feet (1.5 m). A native of northeast Australia, it favors deep, slow-flowing water.

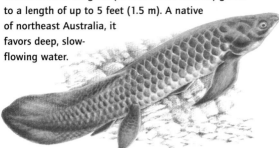

Common name Lungfish

Orders Lepidosireniformes (South American and African lungfish): families Lepidosirenidae (1 sp: South American lungfish, *Lepidosiren paradoxa*) and Protopteridae (4 spp. of African lungfish in genus *Protopterus*); Ceratodontiformes (Australian lungfish): family Ceratodontidae (single sp: *Neoceratodus forsteri*)

Infraclass Dipnoi

Number of species 6

Size From 33 in (85 cm) in spotted lungfish (*P. dolloi*) to over 5 ft (1.5 m) in *Neoceratodus* and over 6.5 ft (2 m) in Ethiopian lungfish (*P. aethiopicus*)

Key features Body elongate with continuous dorsal, caudal, and anal fins; *Neoceratodus* with paddlelike pectoral and pelvic fins and stout body scales; *Lepidosiren* and *Protopterus* with filamentlike pectoral fins, fleshy pelvic fins (filamentlike in *Protopterus*), and smooth scales

Diet Mainly carnivorous, feeding on aquatic animals

Breeding Generally after first rains—before summer rains in Australian lungfish; eggs of African and South American spp. laid in burrows guarded by male, fry have external gills; eggs of Australian lungfish scattered among vegetation, hatch into fry without external gills

Habitat Still pools and deep rivers in Australian lungfish, similar but often shallower waters in other spp.

Distribution Australian lungfish: Murray and Burnett River systems, southwest Queensland, Australia; South American spp: Amazon and Paraná River basins; African spp: widespread in Africa

Status Australian lungfish listed in CITES: Appendix II

Bichirs and Ropefish

The shortfin bichir (*Polypterus palmas palmas*) grows to 12 inches (30 cm) long and feeds mainly on other freshwater aquatic animals. It lives in rivers of Côte d'Ivoire and eastern Liberia.

Common name Bichirs and ropefish

Family Polypteridae

Order Polypteriformes

Subclass Chondrostei

Number of species 10 in 2 genera (*Polypterus, Erpetoichthys*)

Size Smallest: Guinean bichir (*P. ansorgii*) at 11 in (28 cm); largest sp: Congo bichir (*P. endlicheri congicus*) up to 38 in (97 cm)

Key features Elongated body, especially ropefish; head large with flattened front half; snout rounded; eyes small; mouth moderately large; dorsal fin consists of number of finlets with "flag-and-pole" arrangement of spines and rays; pectoral fins with fleshy base; large ganoid body scales; coloration: dull and mottled in many species; attractive dark markings in ornate bichir, with orange-red bands in pectoral fins

Breeding In some species adults move into flooded areas during late summer; individual pairs shed and fertilize 200–300 eggs among vegetation; hatching takes about 4 days; larvae have external gills like amphibian tadpoles

Diet All are hunters, mainly at night, taking insects, other aquatic invertebrates, frogs, and fish

Habitat Shallow water along the edges of rivers, lakes, swamps, and flooded areas, often close to or among vegetation; also waters that have low oxygen content

Distribution Widespread in tropical and subtropical Africa

Status Not threatened

Baltic or Common Sturgeon

Common name Baltic or common sturgeon (Atlantic sturgeon—this common name also applied to another species: *Acipenser oxyrhynchus*)

Scientific name *Acipenser sturio*

Subfamily Acipenserinae

Family Acipenseridae

Order Acipenseriformes

Size Usually 10–11 ft (3–3.4 m) but up to 20 ft (6 m)

Key features Elongated body with distinct snout and heterocercal caudal fin; 5 rows of large, stout scutes, each with a central "spike," along body; underslung mouth with 2 pairs of barbels; coloration: greenish-brown on the back, yellowish-white below

Breeding Migrates from sea to freshwater spawning grounds; spawning occurs in flowing water over gravel; up to 2.5 million eggs abandoned and hatch in less than 1 week; adults return to sea after spawning; juveniles spend up to 4 years in fresh water prior to migrating to sea

Diet Bottom-dwelling marine invertebrates and small fish; does not feed during spawning period

Habitat Mainly shallow coastal waters, usually over sand or mud; some move to deeper waters

Distribution Atlantic Ocean from Norway to North Africa and into western Mediterranean, Baltic, and Black Seas; 1 landlocked population in Lake Ladoga near Leningrad, Russia

Status Listed by IUCN as Critically Endangered; CITES Appendix I; close to extinction in parts of range due to overfishing, accidental catches, pollution, and loss of habitat

Lake Sturgeon

Common name Lake sturgeon

Scientific name *Acipenser fulvescens*

Subfamily Acipenserinae

Family Acipenseridae

Order Acipenseriformes

Size Up to 9 ft (2.7 m) and a weight of 275 lb (125 kg)

Key features Elongated body; pointed snout and underslung mouth; heterocercal tail; long barbels located halfway between tip of snout and mouth; smooth skin between about 36 scutes along the body; coloration: grayish-brown back with darker blotches; similar blotches on the front half of snout; sides and belly whitish

Breeding Migrates upriver in spring to spawn in fast-flowing waters; eggs scattered among gravel, rocks, and boulders, and abandoned; newly hatched larvae remain close to spawning site before drifting downriver

Diet Omnivorous; feeds opportunistically on anything edible; sucks food into its mouth and crunches it to a pulp, repeatedly spitting it out and sucking it back to create pulverized ball soft enough to swallow

Habitat Fresh water in most of range but also brackish habitats in more northern regions; prefers large rivers and lakes over mud, sand, or gravel

Distribution North America from Hudson Bay and Great Lakes south to Mississippi

Status Listed by IUCN as Least Concern; changes to rivers, pollution, and past overfishing probably main factors responsible for decline

Sterlet

Common name Sterlet

Scientific name *Acipenser ruthenus*

Subfamily Acipenserinae

Family Acipenseridae

Order Acipenseriformes

Size Up to 4.1 ft (1.25 m) and 35–42 lb (16–19 kg) in weight

Key features Typical sturgeon shape with heterocercal tail; extended, narrow, pointed snout with underslung mouth; 2 pairs of barbels; lower lip divided into left and right halves; body smooth with 5 rows of bony scutes; scutes along top of the back have curved tips with points directed backward; coloration: dark grayish-brown on back, fading to yellowish white along lower sides of body and belly

Breeding Spawns from mid to late spring; migrates upriver to fast-flowing gravelly areas; lays between 11,000 and 140,000 eggs that hatch in 4–5 days; newborn larvae remain among the gravel for several days before starting to feed, then gradually migrate downriver

Diet Mainly bottom-living invertebrates

Habitat Restricted to fresh and, occasionally, brackish water; usually stays close to river bottom, preferring deeper areas in winter

Distribution Black and Caspian Sea basins; Danube River; rivers draining into Arctic Ocean from White Sea and Sea of Azov

Status Listed by IUCN as Vulnerable; rare owing to fishing, pollution, and changes to river courses; now widely bred in captivity

Beluga

Common name Beluga

Scientific name *Huso huso*

Subfamily Acipenserinae

Family Acipenseridae

Order Acipenseriformes

Size Up to 28 ft (8.6 m) and 2,865 lb (1,300 kg); typical large specimens up to 20 ft (6 m)

Key features Heavy-bodied profile in adults; younger specimens more streamlined; skin membranes bordering gills fused in throat area; wide mouth and 2 pairs of long barbels on snout; scutes not particularly strong and become worn down and partially lost with age

Breeding "Fall" race migrates 300 mi (500 km) or more in September–October to upper reaches of rivers; "spring" race migrates in March–April to middle and lower reaches; both spawn around May over pebble or gravel; up to 7 million eggs laid by a large female; fry hatch in about 1 week; adults return to the sea; juveniles generally move out to sea during their first year

Diet Young beluga feed on invertebrates and small fish; adults feed almost exclusively on fish plus other prey, including waterfowl and, reportedly, seals

Habitat Mainly close to the surface or in midwater regions over fine sediments, often close to estuaries; moves to deeper water during winter—as deep as 590 ft (180 m) in Black Sea

Distribution Adriatic, Black, and Caspian Seas, and associated river systems

Status Some populations classified by IUCN as Endangered; Sea of Azov stock listed as Critically Endangered and Adriatic stock as Extinct; CITES: Appendix II

Pallid Sturgeon

Common name Pallid sturgeon

Scientific name *Scaphirhynchus albus*

Subfamily Scaphirhynchinae

Family Acipenseridae

Order Acipenseriformes

Size Typically 60 in (1.5 m) long and 85 lb (38 kg) in weight

Key features Slim-bodied with pronounced sharp, flat, shovel-shaped snout; 4 barbels in front of mouth; outer barbels nearer mouth than 2 shorter inner barbels; no scales in belly region (unlike closely related *S. platorynchus*); caudal fin markedly heterocercal

Breeding Migrates upriver in spring to breed in swift-flowing shallow streams with gravel beds; spawns late spring and summer (as late as August); adults then return downriver, abandoning eggs

Diet Searches with its flattened snout for worms, mollusks, and other invertebrates buried beneath the surface; will also take small fish if available

Habitat Main river channels that are often cloudy with strong currents and sandy or gravelly beds

Distribution North America, in Missouri River and lower Mississippi River

Status Listed by IUCN as Endangered; numerous management projects along the Missouri have deprived it of many former spawning grounds and of the means of reaching them; damming, impoundment, canalization, and flood control measures have had adverse effects on water temperature and availability of food; CITES Appendix II

American Paddlefish

Common name American paddlefish

Scientific name *Polyodon spathula*

Family Polyodontidae

Order Acipenseriformes

Size Can attain more than 6.6 ft (2 m) in length and over 100 lb (45 kg) in weight; females larger than males

Key features Body elongate and sharklike with unique "paddle" accounting for a third of total length; cavernous mouth; coloration: slate-gray above, often mottled, shading to lighter tones below

Breeding Spawns in April and May, producing up to 750,000 large eggs that hatch in about 1 week; fry free-swimming from the outset

Diet Small drifting invertebrates (zooplankton) and insect larvae; feeds by swimming with huge mouth gaping open and filtering organisms from water with its sievelike gill rakers

Habitat Slow-flowing waters such as oxbow lakes and backwaters more than 4 ft (1.2 m) deep

Distribution North America mainly in Missouri River basin and Gulf slope drainage

Status Listed by IUCN as Vulnerable due to habitat alteration, pollution, and overfishing (the latter especially in the 1980s, when paddlefish were poached for caviar to address shortfall in supplies of sturgeon caviar from war-torn Iran); CITES Appendix II

Alligator Gar

Common name Alligator gar

Scientific name *Atractosteus spatula*

Family Lepisosteidae

Order Semionotiformes

Size Up to 10 ft (3 m)

Key features Sturdy, cylindrical body with short, round-tipped, broad snout; head resembles that of an alligator when viewed from above; ganoid body scales; abbreviated heterocercal tail

Breeding Migrates upriver in spring and summer; few details available, but single female probably spawns with one or more males in depression dug in the bottom; female may lay many thousands of sticky eggs that sink to the bottom and hatch after about 1 week; larvae are sticky and remain near the nest until all egg yolk has been used up

Diet Wide range of fish (including other gars), waterfowl, and crustaceans

Habitat Slow-moving backwaters of large rivers, pools, lakes, swamps, and bayous (marshy bodies of water); mainly found in fresh water but occasionally in brackish water or even sea

Distribution From Mississippi basin in southwestern Ohio and southern Illinois southward to Gulf of Mexico from extreme northwest Florida westward to Veracruz in Mexico

Status Not threatened

Longnose Gar

Common name Longnose gar

Scientific name *Lepisosteus osseus*

Family Lepisosteidae

Order Semionotiformes

Size Up to 6 ft (1.8 m)

Key features Somewhat reptilian in appearance, resembling the long-snouted Asian crocodile (gharial); slender-bodied; narrow, long snout (longest of any gar in relation to head and body); ganoid scales; abbreviated heterocercal tail

Breeding Migrates upriver in early spring; spawning can occur as early as March and extend through summer to August depending on locality; single female may spawn with several males in depression, laying 27,000–77,000 eggs; fry hatch in 6–9 days and adhere to vegetation until yolk sac consumed; males mature at 3–4 years; females may take 6 years.

Diet Predatory, mainly on fish and crustaceans

Habitat Clear, still, or slow-moving waters, including lakes, rivers, and backwaters; often close to vegetation or submerged branches; occurs in brackish water in coastal areas

Distribution Widely distributed from Quebec, Canada, south to central Florida and from Delaware westward to Mexico; also Great Lakes, except Lake Superior

Status Not threatened

Bowfin

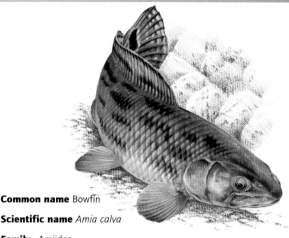

Common name Bowfin

Scientific name *Amia calva*

Family Amiidae

Order Amiiformes

Size Up to 43 in (1.1 m) long and 9 lb (4 kg) in weight

Key features Large head with 2 forward-pointing barbels on snout; sturdy cylindrical body with long-based dorsal fin with some 48 rays; cycloid scales; abbreviated heterocercal tail; coloration: adults dark and drab with a faded eyespot near the base of the top tail fin rays (a black spot surrounded by yellow-orange halo), often barely visible; in juveniles eyespot and halo are brilliantly colored, forming a "false eye" that draws predators' attention away from the head

Breeding In spring; male migrates to shallow water and builds circular matted depression up to 24 in (61 cm) across, often close to tree roots or submerged logs; female lays up to 30,000 eggs that hatch in 8–10 days; eggs and young defended by male for up to 4 months; young grow relatively slowly and may not mature until they are 3–5 years old

Diet Worms, crustaceans, fish, reptiles, and small mammals; juveniles eat plankton, aquatic insects, and planktonic crustaceans

Habitat Lakes, still and slow-moving waters, including swamps; usually near vegetation

Distribution Widespread in eastern North America

Status Not threatened

European and American Eels

The 4.3-foot (1.3-m) European eel (*Anguilla anguilla*) occurs in fresh water in Europe and North Africa, as well as on North Atlantic coasts from Iceland to North Africa and the Mediterranean and Black Seas.

Common name European and American eels

Family Anguillidae

Order Anguilliformes

Number of species 15 in 1 genus (*Anguilla*)

Size Typically up to 3.3 ft (1 m)

Key features Snakelike body; crescentlike gill openings on sides of head, broadening into the base of the relatively large pectoral fin; tiny scales evident on body; complete lateral line extending down both sides of head and body; underside of body lightens from golden yellow to silvery as it matures, with upperparts becoming black; have a strong migratory urge when adult, returning to the sea at this stage; otherwise lives often in slow-flowing stretches of fresh water

Breeding Females lay eggs which hatch into larvae that do not resemble adults

Diet Invertebrates and smaller fish eaten in fresh water

Habitat Young hatch in sea; move to fresh water and return to marine environment to breed themselves (behavior described as "catadromous")

Distribution Widely in much of Europe from the far north down throughout the Mediterranean region (European eel, *A. anguilla*); eastern North America from Labrador down to northern South America (American eel, *A. rostrata*)

Status Both groups are numerous, although numbers have declined significantly in some areas

Spaghetti Eels

A female Edward's spaghetti eel (*Moringua edwardsii*), which at 20 inches (50 cm) grows much larger than the 6-inch (15-cm) males. These eels feed on worms and other invertebrates.

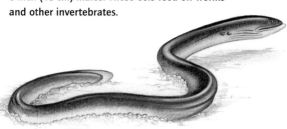

Common name Spaghetti eels (worm eels)

Family Moringuidae

Order Anguilliformes

Number of species At least 6 in 2 genera (*Moringua, Neoconger*)

Size Up to about 3 feet (1 m); in case of Edward's spaghetti eel (*M. edwardsii*) males grow to 6 in (15 cm), females to 20 in (50 cm)

Key features Long, narrow body with no scales; long head with eyes concealed under skin; small pectoral fins on either side of body; gills situated below the midline relatively close to eel's underside; dorsal fin on upper side of body and anal fin below scaled down and resemble folds

Breeding Females conceal themselves largely in shallows; males free-swimming in deeper water; at onset of breeding, fins and eyes of males enlarge, and they migrate inshore to find a mate; females lay eggs; young hatch as free-swimming leptocephali; on transformation to young eels, they hide themselves in seabed

Diet Burrowing marine invertebrates

Habitat Primarily in marine environment, but also in fresh water on occasion—in sandy areas in relatively shallow water, often burrowing head-first into the seabed

Distribution Tropical waters; most species in Indo-Pacific, with *M. edwardsii* and *N. mucronatus* in western Atlantic Ocean from Bermuda and Florida Keys to Bahamas down to northern South America

Status No cause for concern

False Moray Eels

The 7-inch (18-cm) seagrass eel (*Chilorhinus suensonii*) lives in the tropical waters of the western Atlantic from Bermuda and southern Florida south to Brazil. It inhabits sandy areas and seagrass beds, and feeds on small fish and invertebrates.

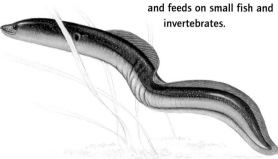

Common name False moray eels

Family Chlopsidae (Xenocongridae)

Order Anguilliformes

Number of species 24 in 9 genera

Size From 6.5 in (16 cm) in collared eel (*Kaupichthys nuchalis*) to 16.5 in (42 cm) in bicolored false moray eel (*Chlopsis bicolor*)

Key features Posterior nostril opening present in lip, with small, rounded gill openings; pores (connecting to lateral line to provide sensory information) present on head but not on body; pectoral fins absent in most species; brown coloration; white inside mouth

Breeding Presumed egg laying; young go through leptocephalus phase; no other details known

Diet Probably invertebrates and small fish

Habitat Marine environment, especially shallow water and reefs

Distribution Predominantly tropical and subtropical parts of Atlantic, Indian, and Pacific Oceans, especially around islands from Seychelles to Hawaii; bicolored false moray eel ranges from coast of Florida to Mediterranean region

Status Unclear; currently not considered under threat

Moray Eels

The 5-foot (1.5-m) undulated moray eel (*Gymnothorax undulatus*) lives on rocky reef flats in the Indo-Pacific from the Red Sea and East Africa to French Polynesia, north to southern Japan and Hawaii, south to Australia's Great Barrier Reef, and east to Costa Rica and Panama.

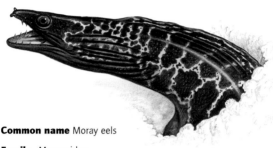

Common name Moray eels

Family Muraenidae

Order Anguilliformes

Number of species About 200 in around 15 genera

Size Largest species recorded (giant moray, *Gymnothorax javanicus*) up to 10 ft (3 m)

Key features Sharp, pointed teeth to grasp small active prey, with a double row of teeth on pharyngeal bones in most species; much blunter dentition pattern for crushing shells in crab-eating morays; some grow to large size and also may be brightly colored; dorsal and anal fins often prominent, but fins reduced to tip of the tail, fusing with caudal fin, in *Gymnomuraena*; tail and head are similar in length; live in lairs rather than in open; often prefer to hunt at night, grabbing unsuspecting prey venturing within reach

Breeding Undocumented, but goes through leptocephalus phase

Diet Carnivorous; techniques to capture prey vary; chain moray (*Echidna catenata*) frequently hunts crabs out of water at low tide

Habitat Relatively shallow waters, usually found in warmer seas associated with reefs; at least 2 species venture into fresh water; only 1 species occurs north of the Mediterranean

Distribution Found in all oceans of the world

Status Generally common

Cutthroat Eels

The 54-inch (1. 4-m) deepwater arrowtooth eel (*Histiobranchus bathybius*), with a depth range of between 2,115 and 17,845 feet (645–5,440 m), occurs in the North Atlantic and North Pacific on the continental slope and abyssal plain. It feeds on fish, crustaceans, and squid.

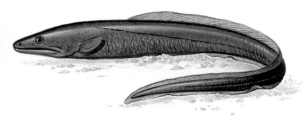

Common name Cutthroat eels

Subfamilies Ilyophinae, Synaphobranchinae, Simenchelyinae

Family Synaphobranchidae

Order Anguilliformes

Number of species About 26 in around 10 genera

Size Recorded up to 63 in (1.6 m)

Key features Dorsal fin in *Histiobranchus* positioned normally, on higher point of the back, but that of *Synaphobranchus* begins much farther back on dorsal surface, corresponding to position of anal fin on ventral surface; gill opening on undersurface of body (unique among eels), resembling an open cut in the throat

Breeding Females produce eggs fertilized by males on breeding grounds; hatch into very distinctive leptocephali that have protruding "telescopic" eyes; may have specific spawning grounds where they congregate in summer, at least in Northern Hemisphere

Diet Active carnivorous hunters of fish and crustaceans, and scavengers of other items such as octopus eggs: can be caught with bait

Habitat Close to seabed in relatively deep cold water down to 13,125 ft (4,000 m); few specimens ever collected

Distribution Atlantic, Indian, and Pacific Oceans

Status Unclear; their habitat makes estimates of numbers difficult

Snipe Eels

The 29.3-inch (74.5-cm) avocet snipe eel (*Avocettina infans*) occurs between 165 and 15,000 feet (50–4,570 m) in all oceans north of about 20° S—including the eastern Pacific from Canada's Queen Charlotte Islands down to central Mexico, but excluding the Mediterranean and the eastern equatorial Pacific.

Common name Snipe eels

Family Nemichthyidae

Order Anguilliformes

Number of species 9 in 3 genera

Size Longest species grow to over 3.3 feet (1 m)

Key features Exceedingly slender, long jaws, with upper longer than lower; jaws much shorter in mature males; jaws also diverge along their length; similarly slender body with large eyes; dorsal and anal fins joined with caudal fin; supraoccipital bone absent from skull; others may be as well, including the pterygoid and palatine; inactive, specialized hunter of small invertebrate prey

Breeding Females lay eggs; spawning is an apparently communal occurrence

Diet Crustaceans, particularly deep-sea shrimp; possibly ectoparasites of other fish; not active hunters; lie vertically in water with open mouth, awaiting passing prey

Habitat Restricted to marine environment, typically at depths from about 5,250 to 16,400 ft (1,600–5,000 m)

Distribution Widely distributed throughout world's oceans; more common in warmer waters but recorded in the Atlantic as far north as Sable Island Bank off Nova Scotia and between Iceland and the Faeroe Islands

Status Probably not especially rare

Conger Eels

The 10-foot (3-m) European conger eel (*Conger conger*) occurs in the eastern Atlantic from Iceland south to Senegal, including the Mediterranean and Black Seas, down to a depth of 1,640 feet (500 m) deep. Found on rocky or sandy bottoms, it moves from the coast into deeper water when an adult.

Common name Conger eels

Family Congridae

Order Anguilliformes

Number of species 150 in 32 genera

Size Largest species recorded at up to 10 ft (3 m)

Key features Even young congers have a dorsal fin that starts above the pectoral fins, extending right down the length of the body; upper jaw protrudes beyond lower, both equipped with large, powerful teeth; no scales evident on skin; capable of adjusting color to match surroundings from grayish-brown upper parts in sandy areas to darker color in rocky crevices

Breeding Essentially undocumented, but pass through a leptocephalus phase; appear to migrate to spawning grounds, e.g., Sargasso Sea; females may produce up to 8 million eggs

Diet Carnivorous; active and aggressive, taking fish and cephalopods unawares

Habitat Often associated with wrecks, reefs, or rocky areas on the seabed

Distribution Atlantic, Pacific, and Indian Oceans

Status Common

Swallower, Gulper, and Pelican Eels

The 3.3-foot (1-m) pelican eel (*Eurypharynx pelecanoides*) is a deepwater species ranging between 1,640 and 24,600 feet (500–7,500 m). It occurs in the eastern Pacific from northern California to Peru. Its mouth is greatly enlarged by a backward extension of its jaws; it feeds mainly on crustaceans.

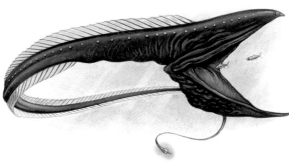

Common name Swallower, gulper, and pelican eels

Families Saccopharyngidae, Monognathidae, Eurypharyngidae

Order Saccopharyngiformes

Number of species 24 in 3 genera

Size From 6.3 in (16 cm) to 6.5 ft (2 m)

Key features All species have a very large mouth and gape, with a distending pharynx, enabling them to swallow correspondingly large prey without apparent difficulty; long, slender tail, often equipped with light-emitting organs; pelican eel (*Eurypharynx pelecanoides*) is unique, being the only bony fish to have 5 gill arches with 6 visceral clefts; vertebral count typically between 100 and 300 bones; swim bladder present; no scales on body

Breeding It is thought that these eels only spawn once in their lifetime, with both males and females dying soon afterward

Diet Fish and other creatures living at great depths

Habitat Deep marine waters

Distribution Widely distributed throughout Atlantic, Pacific, and Indian Oceans

Status Not under any apparent immediate threat from deep-sea fishing

Notacanths

The 24-inch (61-cm) *Halosaurus ovenii*, found at depths between 1,445 and 5,575 feet (440–1,700 m), occurs in the eastern Atlantic (from the Azores and Morocco to South Africa) as well as the western Atlantic (from the Gulf of Mexico and Caribbean to the Lesser Antilles) and is the shallowest-occurring halosaur.

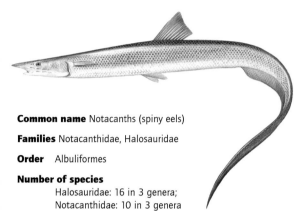

Common name Notacanths (spiny eels)

Families Notacanthidae, Halosauridae

Order Albuliformes

Number of species
Halosauridae: 16 in 3 genera;
Notacanthidae: 10 in 3 genera

Size Up to 10.5 ft (2.5 m)

Key features Relatively slender eel-like body shape; caudal fin largely absent, merged in with the long anal fin on underside of body; swim bladder present; fins reduced to spines in Notacanthidae; pectoral fins located quite high on side of body; some species have light-emitting organs in their bodies; can regenerate lost tips to their tails, which may provide defense against predation

Breeding Leptocephalus grows almost to adult fish size before metamorphosing; larvae previously classified separately under various generic names before their true relationships were appreciated

Diet Invertebrates, including sessile species such as sea anemones; also smaller fish; one species feeds on mud; probably feeds in vertical position

Habitat Deep-sea environment down to a depth of about 17,000 ft (5,200 m)

Distribution Widely distributed throughout all oceans

Status Not under any apparent immediate threat from deep-sea fishing

Atlantic Tarpon

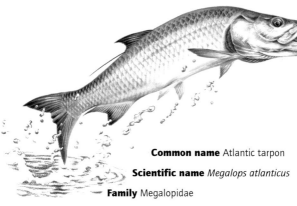

Common name Atlantic tarpon

Scientific name *Megalops atlanticus*

Family Megalopidae

Order Elopiformes

Size Up to 8.25 ft (2.5 m)

Key features Elongated, flattened body shape; large eyes; lower
jaw extends forward from behind eyes; well-forked
caudal fin with a threadlike projection on last ray of
dorsal fin; large silvery scales with a slight metallic blue
coloration over the back; small, sharp teeth throughout
oral cavity; active, lively fish, often congregating in
groups where food supply is plentiful, but not a
schooling species; frequently leaps out of water

Breeding Spawns in shallow waters, producing up to 12 million
eggs; young hatch into ribbonlike leptocephali that
subsequently develop in brackish or even fresh water
where they are able to breathe atmospheric oxygen
directly, which helps them survive in poorly oxygenated
waters (adults also have ability to breathe atmospheric
oxygen); onset of sexual maturity relatively slow at 7–13
years, when they reach 4 ft (1.2 m) long

Diet Carnivorous; primarily fish and cephalopods

Habitat Reef-associated; in fresh, brackish or marine waters;
older tarpon sometimes found in rivers

Distribution Western Atlantic, mainly in tropical seas from
North Carolina down to Brazil; occasionally recorded
farther north up to Nova Scotia; also eastern Atlantic
from Senegal to Angola, exceptional occurrences in
Portugal, the Azores, and France's Atlantic coast

Status Not under immediate threat

African Arowana

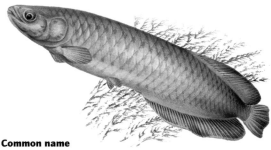

Common name
African arowana

Scientific name *Heterotis niloticus*

Subfamily Heterotidinae

Family Osteoglossidae

Order Osteoglossiformes

Size Up to 38 in (98 cm) long and 24 lb (11 kg) in weight

Key features Elongated body, cylindrical at front and more laterally compressed farther back; long-based dorsal and anal fins; small caudal fin; large head with robust gill covers, large eyes; slightly oblique mouth; body scales relatively large but smaller than in other members of family

Breeding Builds nest some 4 ft (1.2 m) in diameter from vegetation during summer; several thousand eggs, protected by both parents; hatch in about 2 days; fry may have external gills

Diet Small invertebrates filtered from water; special structure called the epibranchial spiral organ helps concentrate food particles and may also help the arowana "taste" water to activate the food-filtering response; will also plunge snout into fine-grained sediments, filters out food particles, and spits out the sand; in addition may eat some plant material such as leaves, roots, seeds, and algae as well as detritus

Habitat Wide range of shallow warm waters, often with mud and dense vegetation

Distribution Widely distributed in all the river basins of sub-Saharan region: Chad, Corubal, Gambia, Niger, Nile, Omo, Volta, Lake Turkana; also introduced to Philippines

Status Not threatened

Arapaima

Common name
Arapaima (pirarucu)

Scientific name
Arapaima gigas

Subfamily Heterotidinae

Family Osteoglossidae

Order Osteoglossiformes

Size Up to 15 ft (4.6 m), but more typically 10 ft (3 m)

Key features Long, powerful body; almost cylindrical in central portion; flattened head with large eyes and cavernous upturned mouth; coloration: variable with grayish, greenish, and bluish hues, and large purple-edged scales, particularly along back; fins have reddish tinge

Breeding October–May depending on location; pair spawn above shallow depression dug in lake or river bed; between 4,000 and 47,000 eggs are laid and incubated in mouth by one parent (probably male), which develops white tubercles on snout; they may produce a nutritious secretion for the fry following release

Diet Mainly fish but also other aquatic vertebrates and even birds

Habitat Large bodies of water, which may be seasonally oxygen deficient; to compensate can gulp air at water surface and then absorb oxygen into the network of blood vessels surrounding swim bladder

Distribution Amazonia

Status Listed as Data Deficient by IUCN; CITES Appendix II; population low or extinct in certain areas owing to heavy fishing, habitat loss, and pollution; captive-breeding programs in operation both for local food source and to satisfy demand for aquarium fish

South American Arowanas

The silver arowana (*Osteoglossum bicirrhosum*) is by far the more common of the two South American arowanas. The pinkish tinge of this young fish is typical of the species. Length to 39 inches (1 m). Arowanas are acrobatic fish that can jump almost 36 inches (90 cm) out of the water to seize flying prey—a trick that has earned them the local name of "water monkeys."

Common name South American arowanas

Scientific name *Osteoglossum* spp.

Subfamily Osteoglossinae

Family Osteoglossidae

Order Osteoglossiformes

Number of species 2 in 1 genus

Size Silver arowana (*Osteoglossum bicirrhosum*) up to 39 in (1 m) but usually smaller; black arowana (*O. fereirai*) up to 24 in (61 cm)

Key features Silver arowana sturdier than black species; both have elongated, sinuous bodies with straight dorsal profile; large, upwardly pointed mouth with 2 chin barbels; large eyes located near top edge of head; dorsal and anal fins have long bases; body scales large and shiny

Breeding Relatively few (200 or fewer) large eggs brooded by male in mouth for 40–60 days; when released, fry can measure 4 in (10 cm) in length

Diet Wide range of prey, particularly insects, spiders, crustaceans, mollusks, and other fish, but also birds, snakes, and even bats

Habitat Flooded forests and lakes; often close to the surface in shallow water near shoreline

Distribution Amazon drainage, western Orinoco, Guyana, and Rio Negro

Status Not threatened

DragonFish

Common name Dragonfish (golden dragonfish, Asian arowana, Asian bonytongue)

Scientific name *Scleropages formosus*

Subfamily Osteoglossinae

Family Osteoglossidae

Order Osteoglossiformes

Size Up to 35 in (89 cm); usually smaller

Key features Compressed, torpedo-shaped body with pointed head; large eyes and mouth; 2 chin barbels; body covered in large, stout scales; 3 main wild color forms: red, gold, and green or silver

Breeding Mating July–December, preceded by long period of courtship and bonding that can last 2–3 months; 30–90 eggs incubated in mouth of male for 5–6 weeks, by which time the fry may be nearly 3.5 in (9 cm) long

Diet Wide range of invertebrates and small vertebrates; feeds mainly at or near water surface but will leap up and snatch prey from overhanging vegetation

Habitat Still or slow-flowing waters that are often turbid or heavily vegetated

Distribution Cambodia, Laos, Vietnam, peninsular Malaysia, Philippines, Indonesia (Kalimantan and Sumatra); introduced to Singapore

Status Listed as Endangered by IUCN; CITES Appendix I

Saratogas

The gulf saratoga (*Scleropages jardinii*) occurs in northern Australia and New Guinea, where it favors clear waters. It can grow to a length of 36 inches (90 cm).

Common name Saratogas

Scientific name *Scleropages* spp.

Subfamily Osteoglossinae

Family Osteoglossidae

Order Osteoglossiformes

Number of species 2 in 1 genus

Size Gulf saratoga (*Scleropages jardinii*) up to 36 in (90 cm) and a weight of 38 lb (17.2 kg); spotted saratoga (*S. leichardti*) up to 36 in (90 cm) and a weight of 9 lb (4 kg)

Key features Gulf saratoga has compressed, powerful body; large mouth with 2 chin barbels; large eyes; pronounced "forehead"; slightly convex back; spotted saratoga has no "forehead" and straighter back; dorsal and anal fins set well back on body

Breeding Between September and December; 30–130 eggs; mouthbrooding occurs in both species; females reported as the brooders in spotted saratoga

Diet Exclusively carnivorous on crustaceans, insects, fish, amphibians, and mice

Habitat Upper reaches of rivers and streams, plus still waters in case of gulf saratoga; mainly near surface, often beneath overhanging vegetation

Distribution Gulf saratoga: northern Australia extending from Jardine River to Adelaide River; also in central and southern drainages of Papua New Guinea and Iran Jaya; spotted saratoga: Fitzroy River of central-eastern Queensland; introduced elsewhere in Queensland, including Mary River

Status Spotted saratoga listed as Lower Risk near threatened by IUCN

African ButterflyFish

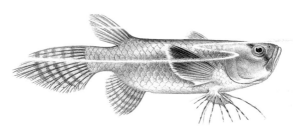

Common name African butterflyfish

Scientific name *Pantodon buchholzi*

Family Pantodontidae

Order Osteoglossiformes

Size 4 in (10 cm)

Key features Straight dorsal profile from snout to small dorsal fin; region from dorsal to caudal fin slightly lower, accommodates folded dorsal fin; caudal fin large and flowing; pectoral fins large and winglike; pelvic fins directly below pectorals, also winglike but to lesser extent; anal fin has extended front and central rays in male; coloration: mottled greenish brown and dark brown; dark band running from the top of head through eye to lower jaw; mouth large and upturned; eyes large and near top of head

Breeding Spawns over several days; male first chases female, then the pair circle each other; male has extended front and central rays to anal fin, giving it a convex profile, a modification that helps in egg fertilization; female releases 200–220 eggs in small batches; eggs float to surface then darken to a deep brown or black color and hatch after 2–4 days, depending on temperature

Diet Mainly surface-living invertebrates and fish; also flying insects snatched from air; unconfirmed reports that it can glide for up to 6 ft (1.8 m) close to the water surface

Habitat Still, shallow waters and swamps

Distribution Western Africa: Cameroon, Nigeria, Republic of Congo

Status Not threatened

Clown Knifefish

Growing to 59 inches (1.5 m), the giant featherback (*Chitala lopis*), like its close relative the clown knifefish, occurs throughout tropical Asia. It varies from bronze to silver in color and lacks the spots of the clown knifefish.

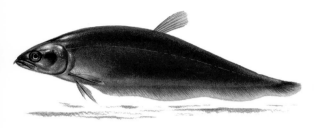

Common name Clown knifefish

Scientific name *Chitala ornata*

Family Notopteridae

Order Osteoglossiformes

Size Up to 39 in (1 m) in length and a weight of 11 lb (5 kg)

Key features Compressed body with small dorsal fin; extremely long anal fin that joins small caudal fin—the "knife"; large eyes; large mouth; distinct hump on mature specimens, making head look small; coloration: grayish-silver with several black spots, each surrounded by a white ring; number of spots varies according to individual and variable even on opposite sides of a single individual; swims using waves that ripple along anal fin

Breeding Several thousand eggs laid on hard substrate such as submerged branch in May–June; eggs guarded and aerated by male; hatching takes 5–6 days

Diet Mainly surface-swimming invertebrates and fish, as well as flying insects that fall into water; hunts usually at night or during twilight of dawn and dusk

Habitat Large and medium-sized rivers, pools, and swampy areas

Distribution Widespread in tropical Asia, including the Mekong Delta (Laos), Cambodia, Malaysia, Java, Sumatra, Thailand, and Myanmar (Burma)

Status Not threatened; Indochina featherback (*C. blanci*) from Cambodia and Thailand listed as Lower Risk near threatened

African Knifefish

The false featherfin (*Xenomystus nigri*) is distinguished from the other African knifefish by its lack of a dorsal fin. It is also smaller, growing to a maximum of 12 inches (30 cm) long.

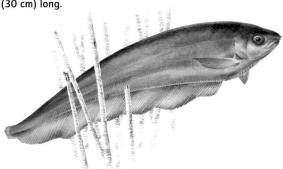

Common name African knifefish

Scientific names *Papyrocranus*, *Xenomystus* spp.

Family Notopteridae

Order Osteoglossiformes

Number of species 3 in 2 genera

Size African featherfin, or African knifefish (*Papyrocranus afer*), up to 32 in (80 cm); *P. congoensis* up to 32 in (80 cm); false featherfin, or African knifefish (*Xenomystus nigri*), up to 12 in (30 cm)

Key features All 3 species have compressed, elongated bodies with large eyes and mouth and characteristic knifelike anal fin joined to small caudal fin; *Xenomystus* has long, tubelike nasal openings; *Papyrocranus* species have small dorsal fin but no pelvics; *Xenomystus* does not have a dorsal fin but has pelvic fins

Breeding *Xenomystus* lays up to 200 eggs, but no details of brood care available; breeding details of *Papyrocranus* not known

Diet Mainly aquatic invertebrates plus flying insects that fall into the water; also take fish

Habitat Mostly relatively quiet waters, often with heavy vegetation and shade

Distribution *Papyrocranus afer* western Sierra Leone to Niger River; *P. congoensis* Congo River; *Xenomystus nigri* widely distributed from West Africa to Nile River

Status Not threatened

Elephantnoses and Whales

The down poker (*Campylomormyrus rhynchophorus*) is a native of the Congo basin in Central Africa, where it grows to 8.5 inches (22 cm) in length.

Common name Elephantnoses and whales

Family Mormyridae

Order Osteoglossiformes

Number of species Around 200 in 18 genera

Size From 3.5 in (9 cm) to 20 in (50 cm)

Key features Laterally compressed body with dorsal, anal, pelvic, and caudal fins well formed; long, narrow extension from back of dorsal and anal fins to base of caudal fin (known as caudal peduncle) and deeply forked tail; mouth extremely variable, ranging from lower lip extended into proboscis or trunk to long snout with small mouth at tip or underslung mouth beneath rounded snout; eyes relatively small; moves and detects prey, food, and mates in dark or murky water by producing weak electrical current from caudal peduncle; pulses bounce off objects, and echoes picked up by receptors in head and front of body

Breeding No details available; differently shaped anal fins in males and females of some species may indicate that close proximity is necessary for effective egg fertilization

Diet Mainly worms and other bottom-living invertebrates

Habitat Frequently in turbid waters with muddy bottoms, often with submerged and above-water vegetation, e.g., shady marshes

Distribution Widely distributed in tropical Africa and the Nile River

Status Not threatened

Aba Aba

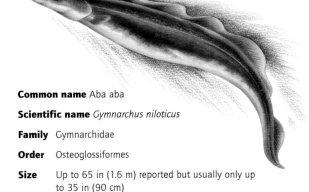

Common name Aba aba

Scientific name *Gymnarchus niloticus*

Family Gymnarchidae

Order Osteoglossiformes

Size Up to 65 in (1.6 m) reported but usually only up to 35 in (90 cm)

Key features Elongated body; relatively large, tapering head with rounded snout; large underslung mouth; small eyes; no pelvic, anal, or caudal fins; dorsal fin with extremely long base containing 183–230 rays; coloration: dark gray along top half, fading to whitish along belly with small dark spots; albinos occasionally reported; weak electric current generated in muscle cells (known as Sach's organ) toward the back of the body help the fish navigate, locate prey, and detect other fish in murky waters

Breeding Builds large elliptical floating nest around 39 in (1 m) in densely vegetated areas like swamps; lays around 1,000 amber-colored eggs; nest guarded by one or possibly both parents; hatching takes about 5 days

Diet Insects, crustaceans, and fish taken at all depths

Habitat Slow-flowing or still waters such as swamps, often with muddy bottoms and turbid water

Distribution Tropical Africa including the Gambia, Nile, Niger, Volta, and Senegal River systems; also Lake Chad and Lake Turkana (Rudolf)

Status Not threatened

Anchovies

The 8-inch (20-cm) Peruvian anchovy (*Engraulis ringens*) occurs in the South Pacific from Peru to Chile at depths between 10 and 260 feet (3–80 m); it stays within 50 miles (80 km) of the coast. The fish is a filter feeder, entirely dependent on the rich plankton found in the Peru Current.

Common name Anchovies

Family Engraulidae

Order Clupeiformes

Number of species About 140 species in 16 genera

Size Up to about 16 in (40 cm) long, but most species much smaller

Key features Small, slender, silvery fish, longer and thinner than herring and rounder in cross section; large snout gives chinless appearance; single, tall dorsal fin halfway along body; symmetrical forked tail; single anal fin; small paired fins; highly gregarious schooling fish; migrate in search of food and spawning areas

Breeding Large, floating, oval eggs produced in spring

Diet Plankton or small prey collected on gill rakers or grasped with small teeth

Habitat Mostly marine in tropical, subtropical, and temperate waters; about 15 percent of all species live in fresh or brackish water

Distribution Atlantic, Pacific, and Indian Oceans and some adjoining seas and rivers

Status Generally not threatened, but many species are fished intensively and need careful monitoring; IUCN lists freshwater anchovy (*Thryssa scratchleyi*) from Australia as Data Deficient; major fisheries include the Pacific anchovy (*Engraulis mordax*), Peruvian anchovy (*E. ringens*), Japanese anchovy (*E. japonica*), and the European anchovy (*E. encrasicolus*)

Wolf Herring

The blackfin wolf herring (*Chirocentrus dorab*) is a long, slender, and voracious predator found in the Indo-Pacific from the Red Sea and East Africa to the Solomon Islands, southern Japan, and northern Australia. It feeds on small schooling fish like herring and anchovies. Males can reach a length of 40 inches (1 m), but females are smaller at around 15 inches (37 cm).

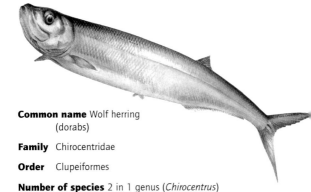

Common name Wolf herring (dorabs)

Family Chirocentridae

Order Clupeiformes

Number of species 2 in 1 genus (*Chirocentrus*)

Size Up to 40 in (1 m) long

Key features Long, narrow body, quite strongly compressed from side to side; covered in light cycloid scales (as in true herring in the family Clupeidae) that are easily dislodged by handling; dark bluish-green on the back and silver on flanks and belly; small dorsal, anal, and paired fins; large forked tail; large eyes; lives in fast-moving schools; may leap clear of water

Breeding Little is known; presumably spawn in schools; larvae develop in surface waters and are as voracious as adults

Diet Highly carnivorous; hunts mostly other fish; prey is tracked by large, sensitive eyes and snared by daggerlike teeth on bottom jaw that project slightly from mouth; mouth opens upward; upper jaw, roof of mouth, and tongue covered in more teeth, so little chance for prey to escape once captured; prey swallowed whole; well-developed gill rakers allow it to take advantage of small prey items as well

Habitat Marine; tropical; upper pelagic

Distribution Indian and western Pacific Oceans

Status Not threatened

Herring

The 10-inch (25-cm) pilchard, or European sardine (*Sardina pilchardus*), occurs in the northeast Atlantic and adjoining seas. It feeds on small crustaceans and other zooplankton.

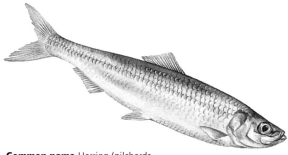

Common name Herring (pilchards, menhadens, sardines, sprats, shad)

Family Clupeidae

Order Clupeiformes

Number of species About 180 species in 56 genera

Size Mostly small fish less than 20 in (50 cm) long; occasionally up to 5 ft (1.5 cm)

Key features Medium-sized, silvery fish with counter shading (dark on back, pale on underside); pelvic fins exactly opposite dorsal fin located along ventral midline; low dorsal fin about halfway along back; forked and notched tail; highly gregarious schooling fish

Breeding Spawn in school at any time of year depending on population; eggs sink and adhere to seafloor; larvae hatch after a week or more; no parental care

Diet Plankton, especially copepods; occasionally fish larvae; food sieved from water and trapped in gill rakers (appendages that partially block the space between mouth and gills)

Habitat Mostly marine and highly migratory; some species migrate into fresh water, others live permanently in rivers or lakes

Distribution Oceans, seas, and rivers worldwide, especially in coastal areas

Status IUCN lists 14 species in family as having various levels of threat: Alabama shad (*Alosa alabamae*) from the U.S. and *Tenualosa thibaudeaui* from Southeast Asia are listed as Endangered. Main species subject of major fisheries are Atlantic herring (*Clupea harengus*), Pacific herring (*C. pallasii*), sprat (*C. sprattus*), Pacific sardine (*Sardinops sagax*), and pilchard (*Sardina pilchardus*)

Black Ghost Knifefish

Common name Black ghost knifefish

Scientific name *Apteronotus albifrons*

Family Apteronotidae

Order Gymnotiformes

Size Grows up to 20 in (50 cm)

Key features Laterally compressed body; no dorsal fin but has a small, distinctive caudal fin (unique among gymnotiform families) organ located near caudal peduncle generates weak electrical currents to help it navigate and locate prey; relatively deep body and corresondingly low-set pectoral fins; also quite a large gape, enabling correspondingly big prey to be taken; anal orifice located on underside of head; black in color, apart from 2 white bands, 1 present on caudal peduncle, the other at base of caudal fin; nocturnal and predatory; not especially social toward its own kind

Breeding Unknown; possibly spawns at start of rainy season and often occurs in late afternoon; female lays relatively few eggs (between 100–200 in total) in batches over a period of about 3–6 hours; male and female do not form permanent pair bond; no parental care displayed

Diet Aquatic invertebrates and fish; young knifefish eat insect larvae at first

Habitat Freshwater rivers

Distribution In both the Amazon and the Paraná Rivers in South America, extending across parts of Ecuador, Peru, Brazil, and Guyana

Status Not threatened

Electric Eel

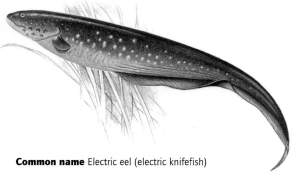

Common name Electric eel (electric knifefish)

Scientific name *Electrophorus electricus*

Family Electrophoridae

Order Gymnotiformes

Size Grows up to 8 ft (2.4 m) long

Key features Large throat; cylindrical teeth; no scales on rounded body; no pelvic fins; anal fin extends around end of tail; approximately 240 vertebrae; remarkable rregenerative powers if injured; can breathe atmospheric air directly; eyes very small relative to body size; prominent electrical organs used to kill prey and to defend itself as well as for communicating via electrical impulses; power generated is enough to kill an animal as big as a horse

Breeding Courtship and egg-laying behavior unknown; males reveal their presence by emitting regular, far-reaching electrical pulses and recognize the shorter responding pulses given off by receptive females

Diet Carnivorous, including shrimp, amphibians, and fish; stuns or kills prey by electrical discharges that can extend up to 3 ft (1 m) in the water; usually hunts after dark

Habitat Confined entirely to fresh water

Distribution Occurs in the Amazon and Orinoco River basins in South America, including Peru, Venezuela, Brazil, and Guyana

Status Not threatened

Mahseers

The mahseer (*Tor tor*), native to Asia, is often found in fast-flowing rivers. Length to 4.9 ft (1.5 m), but most individuals are smaller.

Common name Mahseers

Scientific name *Tor* (about 16 species)

Subfamily Cyprininae

Family Cyprinidae

Order Cypriniformes

Size From around 2.1 in (5.3 cm) to around 9 ft (2.7 m)

Key features Body ranging from relatively slim to high backed; head with large eyes, no scales, and subterminal mouth; 2 pairs of fine barbels; lower lips fleshy; no lip teeth; body scales large in most species; few scales along the lateral line in most species with higher number in small-scaled species; well-formed fins; adipose fin absent; silvery coloration in most species; fins distinctly colored in some species, for example, deep-red pectorals, pelvics, and caudal fins in *T. sinensis*

Breeding Spawning generally late spring or early summer following an upriver migration; eggs generally scattered over gravel or pebbles and abandoned

Diet Wide range of food: large species may feed on fish, crustaceans, and other invertebrates; also plant material, including fruits and algae

Habitat Large, fast-flowing rivers with rocky or gravelly beds; a few species in smaller, slower streams and pools

Distribution Widely distributed in Asia: Afghanistan, India, Bangladesh, Pakistan, Nepal, China, Sri Lanka, Malay Peninsula, Borneo, Sumatra (Indonesia), Java, Thailand, Vietnam, and Laos

Status *Tor yunnanensis* listed by IUCN as Endangered; now much more restricted in its distribution than formerly

Barbs

The rosy barb (*Barbus* [*Puntius*] *conchonius*), native to
Africa and Europe, is usually about 4 in (10 cm) in length
and can be found in both fast- and slow-moving waters.

Common name Barbs

Scientific name *Barbus* spp. (including *Copoëta*, *Puntius*,
and *Barbodes*)

Subfamily Cyprininae

Family Cyprinidae

Order Cypriniformes

Number of species About 700

Size From about 1.2 in (3 cm) to about 14 in (35 cm); most
species under 4 in (10 cm)

Key features Most species have a laterally compressed body,
being deepest (from top to bottom) in region of dorsal
fin; head usually oval shaped and scaleless; 2–4 fine
barbels around mouth; jaws can be extended forward
when opened; dorsal fin located about halfway along
back; anal fin small; well-formed caudal fin; lateral line
runs along midline of body or slightly above it

Breeding Sticky eggs scattered among plants or over the
substratum and then abandoned; hatching may take
1 day but usually takes more than 2 days

Diet Plants, aquatic invertebrates, and insects; larger species
also eat small fish

Habitat Wide range of habitats from clear, flowing mountain
rivers and streams to lowland water courses, ditches,
canals, and flooded fields

Distribution *Barbus* found in Africa and Europe; *Capoëta* found
in North Africa and the Near East; *Puntius* widely
distributed in southern Asia; *Barbodes* mainly in
Indonesia and Sulawesi

Status IUCN lists at least 14 species as Critically Endangered,
4 Endangered, with list growing; over 50 species are
considered under some form of threat mainly due to
habitat pollution

European Barbel

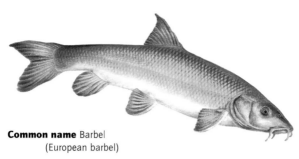

Common name Barbel
(European barbel)

Scientific name *Barbus barbus*

Subfamily Cyprininae

Family Cyprinidae

Order Cypriniformes

Size Up to a maximum of 40 in (1.2 m) and weight of 26.5 lb (12 kg) but usually smaller

Key features Pointed snout; underslung mouth with 2 pairs of fleshy barbels; thick lips; scaleless head; smallish eyes set high on sides of head; elongated body, almost cylindrical in cross-section; back slightly curved, but belly flat; all fins well formed; adipose fin absent; greenish-brown coloration on back, turning to golden along the sides

Breeding Spawning from late spring through summer, following short upstream migration to gravelly areas; up to 50,000 sticky, yellowish, poisonous eggs may be scattered over the bottom and abandoned; hatching takes 10–15 days

Diet Bottom-living invertebrates (especially the larvae of two-winged insects), algae, and detritus; may also take small fish

Habitat Flowing rivers with sandy or gravelly bottoms; also found in pools

Distribution From central and eastern England through France and eastward through Europe to Russia; absent from Scandinavia, Ireland, Denmark, and the Iberian Peninsula (populations present in Spain and Morocco are from introduced stocks)

Status Not threatened

Common Carp

Common name Common carp (European carp, koi)

Scientific name *Cyprinus carpio carpio*; there are also several naturally occurring varieties regarded as subspecies

Subfamily Cyprininae

Family Cyprinidae

Order Cypriniformes

Size Up to around 4 ft (1.2 m) or more in length and a weight of around 82 lb (37.3 kg), but usually smaller

Key features Heavy-bodied fish; fully scaled body; scaleless head with underslung mouth bearing 2 pairs of barbels; well-formed fins; coloration variable but usually greenish-brown on back fading to yellowish-creamish along belly; ornamental varieties (particularly of koi) exhibit wide range of colors

Breeding Season extends from spring into summer; over 1,660,000 sticky eggs scattered among vegetation in shallow water; no parental care; hatching takes 5–8 days

Diet Varied, including vegetation, bottom-living invertebrates, and insects

Habitat Wide range of habitats, particularly larger, slow-flowing or still bodies of water; can tolerate some salt in water; preferred temperature range 37–95°F (3–35°C)

Distribution From its initial central Asian origins the species is now found almost worldwide

Status Although the species *C. carpio* is under no threat of extinction, some of the River Danube populations in a number of countries, e.g., Austria, Hungary, and Romania, are regarded as Critically Endangered; main causes are decreases in range and decline in habitat quality caused by pollutants and other environmental factors; throughout range exploited as food and sport fish, and in some places regarded as a pest due to destruction of plant growth

Goldfish

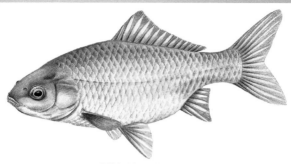

Common name Goldfish (throughout the world); edible goldfish (Malaysia); gibel carp (Kazakhstan); gold crucian carp (Taiwan); golden carp and native carp (Australia)

Scientific name *Carassius auratus auratus*

Subfamily Cyprininae

Family Cyprinidae

Order Cypriniformes

Size Maximum length 23.2 in (59 cm); usually considerably smaller and lighter

Key features Robust, fully scaled body with scaleless head, which is roughly triangular in outline; dorsal fin with 3–4 spines and 15–19 soft rays; anal fin with 2–3 spines and 4–7 soft rays; all fins well formed; no barbels; range of colors—mainly olive-brown to olive-green, but grays, silvers, yellows, golds (with or without blotches), and others also known in wild populations; ornamental varieties exhibit a wide range of colors, finnage, and body shapes

Breeding Many thousands of sticky eggs produced and scattered among vegetation between spring and summer; hatching can take up to 1 week depending on temperature; breeding may involve gynogenesis (stimulation of egg development without fertilization taking place)

Diet Wide-ranging menu, including vegetation and small invertebrates

Habitat Found in a wide range of waters, including lakes, rivers, and ditches; still or slow-flowing waters are preferred, particularly those with soft sediments on the bottom

Distribution Originally from Central Asia, China, and Japan, but introduced virtually throughout the world

Status Not threatened

Grass Carp

Common name Grass carp (white Amur, Chinese grass carp)

Scientific name *Ctenopharyngodon idellus*

Subfamily Cyprininae

Family Cyprinidae

Order Cypriniformes

Size Up to 4.9 ft (1.5 m) in length but often smaller

Key features Elongated body with relatively small head; short snout with subterminal mouth; no barbels; all fins well formed with broad caudal fin; body fully scaled; coloration: generally drab with lighter belly

Breeding Peak of the spawning season occurs in April–May in China; elsewhere there may be some variation; spawning occurs over gravel riverbeds in fast-flowing water; eggs scattered and abandoned; optimum water temperature 81–84°F (27–29°C)

Diet Feeds almost exclusively on aquatic plants and small invertebrates

Habitat Large, still or slow-flowing bodies of water; abundant vegetation is important; low oxygen levels and some salt in water tolerated

Distribution Originally from China and the Amur basin in eastern Siberia; now introduced into around 90 countries from Argentina to New Zealand

Status Not threatened

Freshwater Sharks

The flying fox (*Epalzeorhynchos kalopterus*), native to Southeast Asia as well as India and Africa, can grow to almost 6 ft (1.8 m).

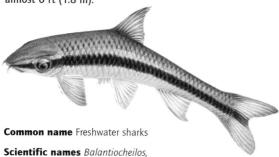

Common name Freshwater sharks

Scientific names *Balantiocheilos, Epalzeorhynchos, Labeo, Luciosoma* (total 116 species)

Subfamilies Cyprininae, Rasborinae

Family Cyprinidae

Order Cypriniformes

Size From 4.8 in (12 cm) to 6 ft (1.8 m)

Key features Considerable variation in body shape: Apollo sharks (*Luciosoma* spp.) elongated with straight backs, upturned mouths, long, fine mouth barbels, dorsal fins set well back on body; silver shark (*Balantiocheilos*) also elongated but has large eyes, large, silvery scales, mouth just under tip of snout, no barbels, groove on back edge of lower lip, and well-formed fins that are yellowish-gold with black edges; in red-tailed black shark, black shark, and relatives (*Labeo* and *Epalzeorhynchos* spp.) mouth suckerlike and located under tip of snout, barbels thicker than in Apollo sharks, back of body generally curved, while belly is flatter and all fins well formed

Breeding Eggs scattered among vegetation or over bottom and abandoned; prespawning migrations may occur

Diet Free-floating and encrusting algae, plants, small invertebrates; terrestial insects and fish (Apollo sharks)

Habitat Mostly found in flowing waters—fast-flowing in the case of some Apollo sharks, e.g., *Labeo spilopleura*, and considerably gentler waters in most others; bottom may be fine-grained, as for some *Labeo* species, or rocky, as for some *Luciosoma* species

Distribution Mostly Southeast Asia but also found in India and Africa (some *Labeo* species)

Status IUCN lists silver shark (*B. melanopterus*), green labeo (*Labeo fisheri*) as Endangered; clanwilliam sandfish (*L. seeberi*) and *L. lankae* as Critically Endangered; and red-tailed shark (*E. bicolor*) as Extinct in the wild, but thousands are captive bred for aquarium trade

Gudgeon

Common name Gudgeon

Scientific name *Gobio gobio*

Subfamily Gobioninae

Family Cyprinidae

Order Cypriniformes

Size Up to 8 in (20 cm) but usually smaller

Key features Slim bodied with largish, pointed scaleless head; mouth subterminal; 1 pair of barbels; back slightly curved; belly flat; well-formed fins, especially the forked caudal; no adipose fin; coloration variable throughout range but basically greenish-brown on the back with spotting, fading to yellowish down sides and onto belly, which can have a purplish sheen; row of dark, roundish blotches along center line of body extending from behind gills to base of tail; fins heavily spotted

Breeding Spawning occurs in spring and summer (April–June); several spawnings can occur in favorable locations; up to 3,000 eggs—but often as few as 800—can be laid in small batches over several days; hatching takes 6–20 days depending on temperature

Diet Predominantly bottom-living invertebrates

Habitat Inhabits variety of waters from fast-flowing rivers and streams with sandy or gravelly bottoms to slow-flowing lowland rivers and larger bodies of still waters, such as lakes and reservoirs

Distribution Naturally distributed throughout Europe, except Ireland, Spain, Portugal, southern Italy, Greece, and parts of Scandinavia; it has, however, been introduced into most of these locations, as well as Morocco; natural distribution extends eastward well into the former U.S.S.R.

Status Not threatened

Danios, Rasboras, and Allies

The zebra danio (*Danio rerio*), native to Southeast Asia, Indonesia, and India, is mostly found in shallow waters. Length to 2.4 inches (6 cm).

Common name Danios, rasboras, and allies

Subfamily Rasborinae (Danioninae)—part

Family Cyprinidae

Order Cypriniformes

Number of species Around 245 in about 25 genera

Size From approximately 0.4 in (1 cm) to 7 in (18 cm)

Key features Most species slim bodied; exceptions include harlequin and fire, golden, or pearly rasbora (*Rasbora vaterifloris*); danios and rasboras carry fine barbels around mouth; fins generally well formed; coloration often silvery based with superimposed patterns

Breeding Most species egg scatterers with appetite for own eggs; a few species deposit eggs on a prepared site, usually the underside of a broad leaf; no parental care is known; hatching takes from 1 to several days

Diet Feeds predominantly on small invertebrates, including flying insects

Habitat Mostly shallow waters in a wide range of habitats, from hill streams to lowland rivers; often found in smaller rivulets and streams, mostly with flowing water

Distribution Widely distributed, mainly in Southeast Asia, Indonesia, and India, with lesser distribution in Africa, China, Amur basin, Japan, and Korea; only 1 species of hill trout, *Barilius mesopotamicus*, found in southwestern Eurasia

Status IUCN lists barred danio (*Danio pathirana*) as Critically Endangered; *R. tawarensis* and *R. wilpita* Endangered; fire rasbora (*R. vaterifloris*) Lower Risk conservation dependent

Bitterlings

Bitterlings (*Rhodeus sericeus*), native to mainland Europe and eastern Asia, have an original way of breeding—they lay their eggs inside a freshwater mussel. Length to 4.3 inches (11 cm).

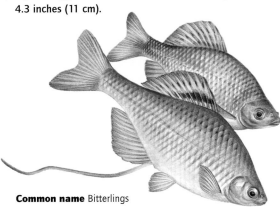

Common name Bitterlings

Subfamily Acheilognathinae

Family Cyprinidae

Order Cypriniformes

Number of species About 15 in 5 genera

Size Most species 2.4–4 in (6–10 cm)

Key features Relatively deep bodied (particularly males); largish silvery scales on body; scaleless head; narrow caudal peduncle; all fins well developed, especially dorsal (in males) and forked caudal fin; coloration: most olive-green on back with silvery scales on sides of body; scales suffused with range of colors

Breeding Generally spawn April–June; eggs usually laid inside freshwater mussel

Diet Wide range of small invertebrates taken both from midwater and bottom zones

Habitat Ponds, lakes, and backwaters of lowland rivers with slow-flowing currents, usually over fine-grained substrata and in vegetated areas; may also occur in more open habitats in turbid water

Distribution Subfamily as a whole ranges from mainland Europe to eastern Asia, including Russia, China, and Japan; some species have been introduced into countries outside their natural range—*Rhodeus sericeus*, for example, now found in U.S., Canada, Britain, Italy, Croatia, and Uzbekistan, while *R. ocellatus ocellatus* has been introduced into China, Japan, Fiji, Korea, and Uzbekistan

Status IUCN lists deepbody bitterling (*Acheilognathus longipinnis*) from central and southern Japan and the Tokyo bitterling (*Tanakia tanago*) from the Kanto Mountains (also in Japan) as Vulnerable; and *A. elongatus* from Lake Dianchi, China, as Endangered

Shiners

The omnivorous red shiner (*Cyprinella lutrensis*) is found in the U.S. and Mexico. It grows to 2.75 inches (7 cm) in length.

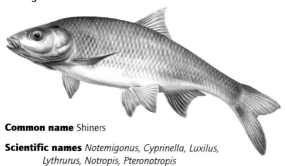

Common name Shiners

Scientific names *Notemigonus, Cyprinella, Luxilus, Lythrurus, Notropis, Pteronotropis*

Subfamily Leuciscinae

Family Cyprinidae

Order Cypriniformes

Number of species 147 in 6 genera

Size Less than 3.5 in (9 cm) to around 12 in (30 cm)

Key features Body generally compressed (flattened from side to side), but to varying degrees, and elongated; well-formed, pointed, scaleless head; well-formed fins, particularly dorsal and caudal, e.g., in bluehead shiner (*Pteronotropis hubbsi*); no adipose fin

Breeding Males of many species develop intensified colors and breeding or nuptial tubercles, mainly in the head region; most species are egg scatterers, but many (particularly *Cyprinella* species) lay eggs in crevices and depressions; hatching takes several days

Diet Mainly small invertebrates; some plant material also taken

Habitat Most species occur in flowing waters, pools, and clear creeks with sandy or rocky bottoms; some species found in vegetated quiet areas, e.g., peppered shiner (*Notropis perpallidus*)

Distribution Widely throughout U.S. and parts of Mexico

Status IUCN lists at least 39 species as under various levels of threat, including 4 species as Extinct in the wild: Ameca shiner (*N. amecae*), Durango shiner (*N. aulidion*), phantom shiner (*N. orca*), and sardinita de Salado (*N. saladonis*)

Minnows and Dace

The European minnow (*Phoxinus phoxinus*) can grow to about 4.5 inches (11.5 cm), but is usually smaller. The dace (*Leuciscus leuciscus*) can reach nearly 12 inches (30.5 cm).

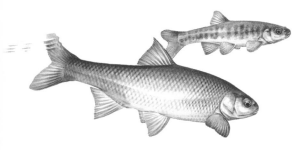

Common name Minnows and dace

Scientific names *Phoxinus, Pimephales, Leuciscus* and other genera

Subfamily Leuciscinae

Family Cyprinidae

Order Cypriniformes

Number of species Around 150 in about 25–30 genera

Size From 2.8 in (7 cm) to 31.5 in (80 cm)

Key features Streamlined body; well-formed eyes; scaleless head; no barbels; well-formed fins; no adipose fin; no true spines on fins

Breeding Eggs usually scattered among vegetation or over rocks, gravel, or sand; usually no parental care; prespawning migrations in many species, with mating taking place in shallow water

Diet From small aquatic invertebrates and insects in smaller species to fish, frogs, and crayfish in larger ones; some plant material also eaten

Habitat Wide range of habitats, including fast-flowing rivers with rocky bottoms and lowland slow-flowing, silt-bottomed waters; almost exclusively fresh water, except European chub (*Leuciscus cephalus*) and some roaches (*Rutilus* spp.)

Distribution North American landmass and Eurasia, with the exception of India and southeastern Asia

Status IUCN lists at least 3 species of *Phoxinus* and 11 species of *Leuciscus* as under threat, including Turskyi dace (*L. turskyi*), probably Extinct

Tench

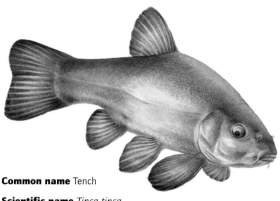

Common name Tench

Scientific name *Tinca tinca*

Subfamily Leuciscinae

Family Cyprinidae

Order Cypriniformes

Size May grow to a length of 33 in (84 cm) and a weight of 16.5 lb (7.5 kg); most specimens usually smaller

Key features Body robust with small scales and thick mucous covering; head relatively large; mouth terminal or just slightly below tip of snout; 1 pair of short barbels; iris of eye red; well-formed fins; no adipose fin; pelvic fins in males considerably larger than in females; coloration ranges from golden-olive to very deep (almost black) olive-green with orange underside; several ornamental color varieties have also been bred

Breeding Main breeding season in natural range extends from May to July; over 800,000 (usually fewer) sticky, greenish eggs laid among plants in shallow, warm water during 2 or 3 spawning bouts spread out over a period of around 2 weeks; hatching takes about 1 week

Diet Aquatic insects, bottom-living invertebrates such as worms, mollusks, and crustaceans; also takes in large quantities of bottom sediments from which small creatures and detritus are filtered out; considerable quantities of plant material also consumed

Habitat Mainly found in slow-flowing or still waters, especially warm lakes and pools with abundant vegetation and a soft, preferably muddy, bottom; may also occur in marshy brackish areas

Distribution Widespread over Europe and eastward to Russia and north into Arctic drainage regions; also widely distributed outside its range

Status Not threatened

Rudd and Roach

The rudd (*Scardinius erythrophthalmus*) and roach (*Rutilus rutilus*) require close examination to tell them apart. Maximum length to about 20 or 21 in (50 or 53 cm).

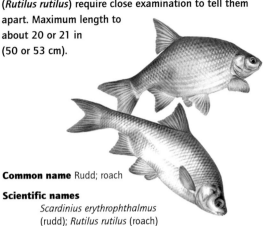

Common name Rudd; roach

Scientific names
Scardinius erythrophthalmus
(rudd); *Rutilus rutilus* (roach)

Subfamily Leuciscinae

Family Cyprinidae

Order Cypriniformes

Size Rudd: up to 20 in (50 cm) long and a weight of around 4.4 lb (2 kg) but often smaller; roach: up to 21 in (53 cm) long and a weight of around 4 lb (1.8 kg), but usually 13.8 in (35 cm) long

Key features Rudd: relatively deep body; smallish, scaleless head; mouth slanted upward; all fins well developed; adipose fin absent; dorsal fin toward rear; iris of eye golden/orange-red; scale keel along belly; coloration: greenish-brown on back, bronze along sides, and creamy along belly; reddish fins; roach: slimmer than rudd; smallish, scaleless head; mouth terminal; all fins well developed; adipose fin absent; dorsal fin central; iris of eye red; coloration: bluish- or greenish-brown on back with silvery sides; dusky dorsal and caudal fins; pelvics and anal orange to red; reddish pectorals

Breeding Both species breed between April and June; both egg scatterers; rudd eggs take 8–15 days to hatch; roach eggs take 9–12 days; rudd females may lay up to 200,000 eggs (usually fewer); roach females produce around 15,000 eggs, maximum 100,000

Diet Both species feed on insects, small crustaceans, and plant matter

Habitat Rudd: slow-flowing or still waters; also found in lowland rivers and lakes; roach: generally similar and also faster-flowing waters

Distribution Rudd: widespread across Europe north of the Pyrenees and eastward to middle Asia; roach: widely distributed in Europe as far east as the Urals

Status Not threatened

Chinese Algae Eater

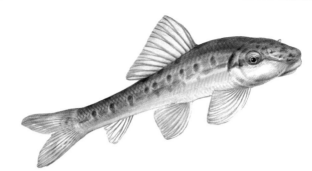

Common name Chinese algae eater (sucking loach, Indian algae eater, algae eater)

Scientific name *Gyrinocheilus aymonieri*

Family Gyrinocheilidae

Order Cypriniformes

Size Up to 12 in (30 cm) reported but usually smaller

Key features Elongated body; head with sloping forehead and underslung suckerlike mouth; barbels absent; gill opening divided into 2: an upper, small inhalant opening and a lower, exhalant opening

Breeding No details available of spawning in the wild, although some have spawned in captivity

Diet Predominantly consists of encrusting algae, but also includes insect larvae and zooplankton

Habitat Fast-flowing, oxygenated mountain streams with rock- or pebble-strewn bottoms; fish attaches itself to rocks by suckerlike mouth to avoid being swept away; gills with inhalant opening as well as exhalant opening allow fish to extract oxygen from water, even though mouth is blocked by the sucker; gill covers beat at up to 230 times a minute to generate water flow over gills

Distribution Mainly Thailand (from where all wild-caught specimens exported for aquariums originate); also known from Laos, Cambodia, China, and Vietnam

Status Not threatened

Chinese Sailfin Sucker

Common name Chinese sailfin sucker (Chinese sucker, Chinese high-fin sucker, Chinese shark, sailfin sucker, topsail sucker, Asian sucker, Hilsa herring, rough fish)

Scientific name *Myxocyprinus asiaticus*

Subfamily Cycleptinae

Family Catostomidae

Order Cypriniformes

Size Up to around 39 in (1 m) but usually smaller, at around 24 in (61 cm)

Key features Juveniles with small head, downturned mouth, high back, flat belly, sail-like dorsal fin, well-formed caudal fin, compressed body (flattened from side to side), and attractive dark-light banding or mottling; as they develop into adults, sail-like character of dorsal fin becomes less pronounced, head remains relatively small in relation to body, body becomes proportionately less deep but still retains hump-backed shape, banding becomes less distinct, and fins become very dark, i.e., chocolate-brown to almost black

Breeding No details of natural spawnings available; can be bred for aquacultural purposes by injecting with hormones, and the eggs and sperm later removed by stripping (gently squeezing the eggs from the bodies of pregnant females and sperm from males)

Diet Mostly bottom-dwelling invertebrates and plant matter

Habitat Mainly found in cool, flowing rivers, often over fine-grained substrata

Distribution Centered around the Yangtze River and Huang Ho River drainage in eastern China

Status Not threatened

North American Suckers

The razorback sucker (*Xyrauchen texanus*), once extremely abundant in the U.S., is now in danger of extinction. Length to 36 inches (91 cm).

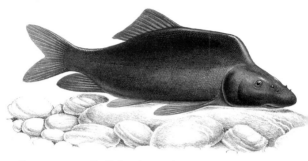

Common name North American suckers

Subfamilies Cycleptinae (part), Letiobinae, Catostominae

Family Catostomidae

Order Cypriniformes

Number of species 68 in about 13 genera

Size From around 6.5 in (16.5 cm) to 40 in (1 m)

Key features Body generally long and relatively slim but highbacked in a few species; head scaleless; underslung mouth and fleshy lips wrinkled or bear papillae except in extinct harelip sucker (*Moxostoma lacerum*); no lip teeth; well-formed dorsal fin with long base in buffaloes (*Ictiobus* spp.), quillback (*Carpiodes cyprinus*), carpsuckers (*C. carpio* and *C. velifer*), and blue sucker (*Cycleptus elongatus*); no adipose fin; well-formed tail

Breeding Spring upriver spawning migrations reported for many species; eggs usually scattered in shallow water and often over pebbles or gravel; no parental care reported

Diet Mostly small invertebrates filtered from bottom sediments and "vacuumed up" with fleshy-lipped, suckerlike mouth

Habitat Most species occur in cool running waters, often with rocky bottoms, in small or medium-sized rivers, or in clear pools; some *Catostomus* species prefer shallower mud- or soft-bottomed pools and creeks; a few occur in lakes, swamps, and ponds with muddy, silty, or sandy bottoms

Distribution Majority exclusively in U.S. and Canada; others extend into Mexico; longnose sucker (*Catostomus catostomus*) also in Siberia

Status IUCN lists nearly 30 species as under varying levels of threat; at least 2 species—Snake River sucker (*Chasmistes muriei*) and harelip sucker (*Moxostoma lacerum*) driven to extinction over past century or so

Kuhli Loaches

The kuhli loach (*Pangio kuhlii*) is native to Thailand, Sumatra, Borneo, Malaya, Indonesia, and Java. Length to 4.7 inches (12 cm).

Common name Kuhli loaches (coolie loaches)

Scientific name *Pangio* spp.

Subfamily Cobitinae

Family Cobitidae

Order Cypriniformes

Number of species 22

Size Details not available for all species; smallest may be *P. incognito* from Sarawak in Malaysia, at around 1.2 in (3 cm); largest known are eel loach (*P. anguillaris*) and kuhli loach (*P. kuhlii*), both of which grow to 4.7 in (12 cm)

Key features All have elongated bodies, some more eel-like than others; head scaleless; eyes small and covered with transparent skin layer; 1 erectile spine under each eye; mouth subterminal; 4 pairs of barbels, 1 pair of which is on the "nose"; dorsal fin well behind a vertical line drawn upward from the pelvic fins; no adipose fin; dorsal fin almost straight edged; coloration variable in many species, particularly banded ones like half-banded loach (*P. semicincta*), Kuhli loach (*P. cuneovirgata*), and others

Breeding Few details known; in some species, e.g., Java loach (*P. oblonga*), spawning may occur in very shallow water in flooded forests; in aquarium spawnings of the slimy, or Myer's, loach (*P. myersi*) green eggs have been scattered among plant roots, stems, or floating vegetation

Diet Where food preferences are known, most found to eat small, bottom-dwelling invertebrates

Habitat Most in flowing waters over fine-grained bottom and abundant leaf litter; some prefer shady forest streams and rivers

Distribution Most originating in the Malay Peninsula and Indonesia, with a couple—both known as the Indian kuhli, or coolie loach—found in India

Status Not threatened

Clown Loach

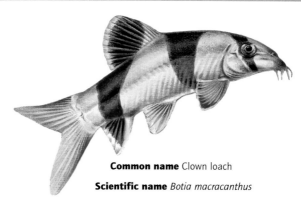

Common name Clown loach

Scientific name *Botia macracanthus*

Subfamily Botiinae

Family Cobitidae

Order Cypriniformes

Size Up to 16 in (40 cm); most specimens attain a size of around 12 in (30 cm)

Key features Pointed, scaleless head with subterminal mouth bearing 2 pairs of rostral barbels; 1 erectile spine under each eye; body compressed; fins well formed, especially caudal fin; adipose fin absent; coloration: orange base color with 3 broad black bands, the first of which passes from top of head through eye and cheeks to "chin" area; second broader—anterior edge starting immediately behind first band and posterior just in front of dorsal fin, this band narrows as it extends downward to end behind pectoral fins; third band covers most of dorsal fin and back, narrowing and extending through anal fin

Breeding Very little known about breeding habits; upriver migrations occur just prior to high-water season; spawning occurs in fast-flowing stretches of rivers; eggs probably hidden under rocks or scattered among crevices; no parental care occurs

Diet Feeds predominantly on bottom-dwelling invertebrates, including (particularly) worms and crustaceans; also takes some plant matter

Habitat Flowing rivers in Kalimantan (Borneo) and Sumatra (Indonesia); in Kalimantan species normally found in brown- or black-water rivers with few suspended sediments; in Sumatra tends to be found in turbid waters; substrate usually contains rocks, pebbles, and sandy areas

Distribution Kalimantan and Sumatra; also introduced into Thailand and Philippines, but these introductions may not have become established

Status Not threatened

Weather Loach

Common name Weather loach (European weather loach, pond loach, weather fish)

Scientific name *Misgurnus fossilis*

Subfamily Cobitinae

Family Cobitidae

Order Cypriniformes

Size Up to a maximum of nearly 14 in (35 cm) but usually a little smaller

Key features Elongated, eel-like body; smallish head with underslung mouth; 5 pairs of barbels; smallish eyes located high on side of head; erectile spine under each eye; sightly rounded dorsal and caudal fins; small anal fin; adipose fin absent; body covered in thick slime; dull light-brown coloration with several dark bands extending from behind head to base of caudal fin

Breeding Spawning from April to June among plants in shallow water; egg laying may extend over several weeks with as many as 170,000 eggs reported (although much smaller spawns are more common); hatching 8–10 days; newly hatched larvae have small, ribbonlike external gills that help them breathe in oxygen-poor waters into which they are frequently born

Diet Bottom-living invertebrates, including worms, mollusks, and insect larvae; some plant material may also be eaten; mainly active from dusk; inactive in daytime except when atmospheric pressure drops, as when storm approaching, at which time becomes hyperactive

Habitat Mainly lowland still waters like floodplains, backwaters, ponds, and marshes—areas that may have fine-grained bottoms with low levels of oxygen, and that may dry up; usually these habitats also heavily vegetated

Distribution Widely distributed in Europe from France, Denmark, and Holland as far eastward as Caspian Sea; absent from southern areas, British Isles, and Scandinavia

Status Not threatened

River or Torrent Loaches and Allies

Torrent loaches (*Gastromyzon* species) are native to Asia, mostly Borneo, and some species reach 4 inches (10 cm) in length.

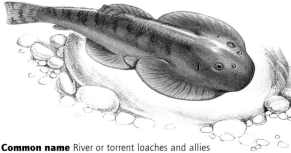

Common name River or torrent loaches and allies

Family Balitoridae (Homalopteridae)

Order Cypriniformes

Number of species Around 470 in around 53 genera

Size Most species around 4–6 in (10–15 cm); some around 2 in (5 cm)

Key features All species elongate to some degree—some almost eel-like, especially in Noemacheilinae (stone loaches and allies); 2 general body shapes in Balitorinae (flat loaches): tribe Balitorini have elongated, not excessively flattened bodies; 2 or more unbranched front rays in pectoral and pelvic fins; tribe Gastromyzontini have less elongated bodies but with significantly depressed front part; 1 unbranched front ray in pectoral and pelvic fins; fins generally circular and together with fold of skin that extends between them form suckerlike structure; in Balitorinae head has underslung mouth bearing 3 or more pairs of barbels; fins generally well formed, some modified into suckers; caudal fin often with longer lower lobe in species inhabiting areas of strong currents

Breeding Breeding behavior unknown for Balitorinae; better known in some Noemacheilinae: adults usually gather at spawning grounds; up to 80,000 eggs produced in some species; eggs scattered among plants; hatching takes 14–16 days

Diet Mostly bottom-living invertebrates; many species from torrential streams feed primarily on encrusting algae

Habitat Most species found in flowing water whose force may range from gentle currents to torrents; bottom mostly rocky or pebbly but may be fine grained and vegetated in some instances, e.g., in some stone loach habitats

Distribution Widely distributed throughout Europe and Asia

Status IUCN lists 26 species as under various levels of threat

Stone Loach

Common name Stone loach

Scientific name *Noemacheilus*
(*Nemacheilus*) *barbatulus*

Subfamily Noemacheilinae (Nemacheilinae)

Family Balitoridae (Homalopteridae)

Order Cypriniformes

Size Up to 6 in (15 cm); usually about 4 in (10 cm)

Key features Elongated body; front half almost cylindrical in cross-section, becoming flattened side to side farther back; moderately sized head and eyes; eye spine absent; small, ventrally placed mouth with 3 pairs of barbels: 2 on upper lip and 1 at each corner of mouth; tiny nonoverlapping scales on body; well-formed fins, tail fin relatively large and almost straight edged; greenish-brown color along back with irregular patches, fading to lighter colors along sides of body; yellowish belly

Breeding Unusually, both sexes may develop nuptial tubercles on pelvic fins (more prominent in males) during breeding season (April–June in most areas); breeding adults may gather at spawning ponds; up to 80,000 eggs may be laid by large females in 2–3 batches; eggs usually scattered among plants or stones; some reports indicate that eggs may be deposited in a cavity and may be guarded by female; hatching takes about 14–16 days; young may take 2–3 years to mature

Diet Mainly bottom-dwelling invertebrates; may also feed on fish eggs and some plant matter

Habitat Mainly central and upper reaches of flowing watercourses with clear waters of varying chemical composition but relatively pollution free and with generally high levels of dissolved oxygen; also found in ponds, quarries, and lakes; also occurs in vegetated waters; frequently found over rocky or pebbly substrata but may also occur over fine-grained sediments

Distribution Widely distributed from Ireland, where it was introduced, eastward through Europe all the way to China, with a few notable exceptions

Status Not threatened

Citharinids

The pike characin (*Phago loricatus*) lives in African rivers, where it darts from cover to attack unsuspecting prey— often biting a chunk from a victim and then hastily retreating. It grows to 6.5 inches (16.5 cm).

Common name
Citharinids

Subfamilies Distichodontinae, Citharininae (moonfish and allies)

Family Citharinidae

Order Characiformes

Number of species Around 102 in about 20 genera

Size From about 0.8 in (2 cm) to 33 in (84 cm)

Key features Body variable: long, slim, and streamlined in pike characins (e.g., *Phago* spp.) to oval or almost circular in some moonfish; head variable: sharply pointed, with movable upper jaw in some species to rounded in distichodins (e.g., *Distichodus* spp.); eyes large; mouth usually situated at tip of snout (terminal) but slightly underneath in some species; teeth generally pointed, but moonfish lack teeth; all fins well formed; coloration extremely variable, ranging from silvery body with reddish fins to heavily banded

Breeding Few details; spawning mainly during summer season; spawning may be preceded by an upriver migration; eggs are scattered and abandoned; hatching about 1 day in some tetras

Diet Moonfish and most distichodins are plant eaters; tetras and darters (e.g., *Neolebias*, *Nannocharax*, and *Nannaethiops* spp.) feed on small invertebrates; pike characins feed on insects or fish

Habitat Smaller species in streams either among vegetation or on or near bottom; large species often in lakes; darters prefer margins of larger fast-flowing rivers; predatory species often in large vegetated bodies of water

Distribution Widely in western, central, and southern Africa

Status Not threatened

Hemiodids

Hemiodus argenteus sports the large forked tail typical of characins. This species grows to a length of 9 inches (23 cm) or more.

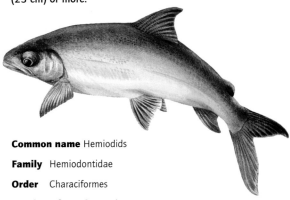

Common name Hemiodids

Family Hemiodontidae

Order Characiformes

Number of species 28 in 5 genera

Size From 3 in (7.6 cm) to around 12 in (30 cm); most between 4–12 in (10–30 cm)

Key features Elongate, torpedo-shaped body for fast swimming; almost cylindrical in cross-section; pointed head; mouth located under tip of snout; small lower jaw with no teeth except in *Micromischodus sugillatus*; large eyes; fins well formed, tail large, powerful, and forked; coloration: silvery body, central black body spot, with or without back line extending to the base of tail; tail with colored edges

Breeding Few details; breeding during rainy season; all species are egg scatterers

Diet Tiny organisms picked off plants or rocks (*Hemiodus* spp.); sandsuckers and jatuarainas (*Bivibranchia* and *Argonectes* spp.) dig in mud or sand for tiny creatures, using extensible upper jaw; others feed on plants and plant debris; 2 *Anodus* species filter tiny organisms and algae from water using large number (up to 200) of very fine gill rakers

Habitat Flowing water up to rapids; water always highly oxygenated; bottoms sandy or rocky and may contain aquatic plants

Distribution Amazon, Orinoco, and Paraná basins

Status Not threatened

Curimatas and Flannelmouths

The 3.5-inch (9-cm) diamond spot curimata (*Cyphocharax spilurus*) is widespread in South America. It is one of several species with a conspicuous dark spot near the tail region. The fish lives in fast-flowing rivers and feeds on detritus.

Common name Curimatas and flannelmouths

Subfamilies Curimatinae (curimatas), Prochilodontinae (flannelmouths)

Family Curimatidae

Order Characiformes

Number of species Curimatinae: over 100 in 8 genera; Prochilodontinae: over 20 in 3 genera

Size Curimatinae: about 1.4 in (3.5 cm) to 10.6 in (27 cm); Prochilodontinae: 10 in (25 cm) to 29 in (74 cm)

Key features From elongate with distinct back and belly to deep bodied; head varies from rounded to pointed snout; mouth at tip of or under snout; fleshy lips form sucking disc in Prochilodontinae; no jaw teeth in Curimatinae; small jaw teeth in Prochilodontinae; eyes large; fins well formed, large tail forked; coloration variable, but silvery scales common; several Curimatinae have long, black body line or tail spot; some Prochilodontinae have marked tails with black and light-colored horizontal bands; dorsal and anal fins well marked

Breeding Some spawn in shoals; some spawn in turbid water in main river channels following migration from surrounding areas beginning or during rainy season; in southern regions spawning in headwaters after upriver migration at beginning of flood season; all are egg scatterers

Diet Encrusting algae, plant fragments, and detritus; some small invertebrates

Habitat From coastal rivers to ponds

Distribution Wide-ranging in southern Central America and South America

Status Not threatened

Headstanders

The 4.7-inch (12-cm) striped headstander (*Anostomus anostomus*) lives in the Amazon and Orinoco basins. It is usually found head-down in well-oxygenated waters. It is a member of the subfamily Anostominae.

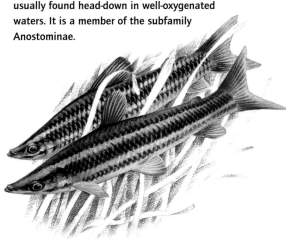

Common name Headstanders

Subfamilies Anostominae, Chilodontinae

Family Anostomidae

Order Characiformes

Number of species Anostominae: 128 in 10 genera; Chilodontinae: 5 in 2 genera

Size From 3.2 in (8 cm) to 16 in (40 cm)

Key features Most species have elongated body, cylindrical in cross-section; notable exceptions: high-backed headstander (*Abramites hypselonotus*) and spotted headstander (*Chilodus punctatus*); head with extended snout ending in small mouth, often with fleshy modifications; in leporins (*Leporinus* spp.) the teeth and lip arrangement creates a "hare-lip" effect; mouth upturned in some species, e.g., members of genus *Anostomus*; eyes large; fins well formed; adipose fin present in all species; body patterns include vertical bands, spots, and longitudinal bands

Breeding Information lacking; spawning migrations upriver may occur; eggs scattered, often among vegetation, and abandoned; hatching takes several days

Diet Plants, including algae; some species feed on insects and other invertebrates

Habitat Variety of waters with medium to strong current; vegetation is often preferred; rocks and clefts are headstander habitats, as well as "blackwater"

Distribution Widely in tropical South America

Status Not threatened

Splashing Tetras and Pencilfish

The three-lined pencilfish (*Nannostomus trifasciatus*) rarely exceeds 2 inches (5 cm) in length. In the wild it feeds on worms, crustaceans, and small mollusks.

Common name Splashing tetras and pencilfish

Subfamilies Pyrrhulininae (splashing tetras and pencilfish), Lebiasininae (voladoras)

Family Lebiasinidae

Order Characiformes

Number of species Pyrrhulininae: 43 in 5 genera; Lebiasininae: 19 in 3 genera

Size From 0.8 in (2 cm) to 7 in (18 cm)

Key features Body elongated, cylindrical in cross–section; in pencilfish snout extended and ends in a tiny mouth held partially open; in the voladoras mouth longer and directed slightly upward; eyes large; fins well formed; adipose fin absent in some voladoras; coloration variable: all pencilfish (except cross-banded pencilfish, *Nannostomus espei*) have dark body lines running from snout to tail, often with golden or red lines above or below each dark band; splashing tetra (*Copella arnoldi*) and relatives often have blue or other small spots on lighter background

Breeding Most scatter eggs among submerged vegetation; some lay eggs on submerged broad-leaved plants or in a depression and males guard eggs until they hatch; splashing tetra lays eggs above water surface; hatching takes about 3 days, depending on species

Diet Insects and aquatic invertebrates; some, e.g., *Lebiasina* species, eat large quantities of mosquito larvae

Habitat Streams, away from strong currents, often with overhanging and submerged vegetation, sunken branches and twigs, fine-grained bottom covered in leaf litter

Distribution Tropical South America, including Ecuador, Colombia, Brazil, Guianas, Venezuela, Surinam, and Peru

Status Not threatened

Trahiras and Pike Characoids

The kafue pike (*Hepsetus odoe*), a lethal predator of African rivers, builds a bubble nest at the water surface into which eggs are deposited. The eggs are guarded by one or both parents. Length to 28 inches (70 cm).

Common name Trahiras and pike characoids

Families Erythrinidae (trahiras), Ctenoluciidae (gar or pike characins), Acestrorhynchidae (cachorros), Hepsetidae (kafue pike)

Order Characiformes

Number of species Erythrinidae: 13 in 3 genera; Ctenoluciidae: 7 in 2 genera; Acestrorhynchidae: 15 in 1 genus; Hepsetidae: 1 species

Size From around 2.8 in (7 cm) to 40 in (1 m)

Key features Powerful body; large eyes; trahiras have blunt heads, other families have elongated snouts; large mouths, powerful jaws, and sharp teeth; fins well formed; tail powerful—rounded in trahiras, forked in others; coloration: mottled or drab in trahiras; gar characins color variable; cachorros silvery along sides of body; kafue pike (*Hepsetus odoe*) olive green-brown shades above, fading to lighter colors

Breeding Either little known or incomplete; most spawn at onset of rainy season; kafue pike spawns several times during summer, builds bubble or foam nest, lays thousands of eggs guarded by parents; hujeta (*Ctenolucius hujeta*) scatters over 1,000 eggs; hatching takes 1 day; female *Hoplias aimara* carries 6,000–60,000 eggs

Diet Predatory; juveniles feed on insects and small fish; most adults feed on fish and some insects

Habitat Streams to larger rivers, backwaters, lakes, and swamps; trahiras in standing water; gar characins and cachorros close to surface; kafue pike in deep, quiet water

Distribution Erythrinidae, Ctenoluciidae, and Acestrorhynchidae: tropical South America; Hepsetidae: tropical Africa, but not in Nile River, Congo River in Zambia, or Great Rift Lakes

Status Not threatened

Freshwater Hatchetfish

The marbled hatchetfish (*Carnegiella strigata*) occurs in the Guyanas and Amazon River basin. Although a few other fish species can glide out of water, only hatchetfish use propulsive force to move through the air. Length to 1.4 inches (3.5 cm).

Common name Freshwater hatchetfish

Family Gasteropelecidae

Order Characiformes

Number of species 9 in 3 genera

Size From 1 in (2.5 cm) to 3.2 in (8 cm); aquarium-reared specimens slightly larger

Key features Body with pronounced chest enlargement and keel; head with flat top, upwardly directed mouth; large eyes; dorsal profile straight to dorsal fin; all fins well developed; pectoral fins extremely large and winglike—when confronted by predators it can leap from water and fly a short distance by flapping them; all species have silvery scales on side of body; several species have dark central body line extending to caudal peduncle

Breeding Eggs scattered among roots of floating plants and among vegetation and then abandoned; hatching takes 1.5 days

Diet Lives most of the time just beneath the water surface and picks off insects that fall in; also eats aquatic invertebrates

Habitat *Carnegiella* in small streams and creeks; *Gasteropelecus* and *Thoracocharax* in open waters

Distribution Panama in Central America; South American countries except Chile

Status Not threatened

African Tetras

At 4.5 ft (1.3 m) in length and weighing110 pounds (50 kg) the tigerfish (*Hydrocynus goliath*) is the biggest member of the family Alestidae. This large, streamlined fish with fanglike teeth is a voracious predator of the Zaire River.

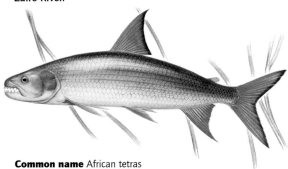

Common name African tetras

Family Alestidae

Order Characiformes

Number of species Around 110 in 18 genera

Size From 0.8 in (2 cm) to 4.5 ft (1.3 m); most within range of 2–4 in (5–10 cm)

Key features Body elongate and compressed, some species with hump behind head and deeper body, e.g., African moonfish (*Bathyaethiops caudomaculatus*); mouth armed with pointed teeth; fins well formed; forked caudal fin in all species; coloration variable, usually includes bright silvery sides to body; many possess black blotch or streak on caudal peduncle

Breeding Spawning late spring to early fall; eggs scattered over bottom and abandoned; hatching from15 hours to 6–7 days, e.g., eggs of tigerfish (*Hydrocynus goliath*) hatch in 15–22 hours, while Congo tetra (*Phenacogrammus interruptus*) eggs take 6 days or more

Diet Predatory; larger species feed on other fish; smaller ones on insects and other aquatic invertebrates; plant material also eaten

Habitat Fresh waters from streams and pools to large lakes, e.g., Lakes Chad, Albert, Turkana, and Malawi

Distribution Tropical Africa

Status Not threatened

Predator Tetras and S. American Darters

The sailfin tetra (*Crenuchus spilurus*) of Guyana and the middle Amazon region grows to a length of about 2.5 inches (6 cm). Males (shown here) have larger dorsal fins than females.

Common name Predator tetras and South American darters

Subfamilies Crenuchinae (predator tetras and sailfin tetra), Characidiinae (darters)

Family Crenuchidae

Order Characiformes

Number of species Crenuchinae: 3 in 2 genera; Characidiinae: around 74 in 9 genera

Size From 1.2 in (3 cm) to about 4 in (10 cm)

Key features Two distinct body forms: Crenuchinae have large mouths and (in males) large dorsal and anal fins; eyes large; head large; predator tetras have no adipose fin; body compressed; fins well formed; coloration: golden line running the length of body; large black spot on caudal peduncle and red edges to fins in males; fins are also heavily spotted in creamy yellow; predator tetra (*Poecilocharax weitzmani*) vividly marked with colored lines and spots; sides of body have scattered luminous green scales; Characidiinae have long, slim bodies and lack extra-large mouth of Crenuchinae; coloration generally drab with mottled or banded patterns in shades of brown; sides may be whitish or creamish

Breeding Detail lacking; eggs of sailfin tetra (*Crenuchus spilurus*) laid on a stone and fanned by male; darters scatter eggs over substrate and abandon; hatching about 2 days

Diet Insects and invertebrates; larger species eat smaller fish

Habitat Small streams with fast-flowing water, some darter tetras live in fast-flowing rapids and falls, often clinging to bottom rocks or vegetation

Distribution Tropical and subtropical South America from eastern Panama to La Plata in Argentina

Status Not threatened

South American Tetras

The blind cave characin (*Astyanax jordani*) is found in limestone caves in Mexico. It grows to a length of about 3.5 inches (9 cm).

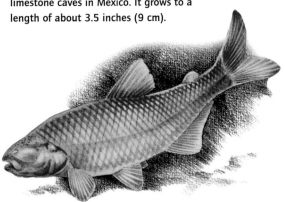

Common name South American tetras

Subfamilies Tetragonopterinae, Cheirodontinae

Family Characidae

Order Characiformes

Number of species Tetragonopterinae: 2 in 1 genus; Cheirodontinae: around 30 in 14 genera

Size Most less than 2.4 in (6 cm); smallest around 1.2 in (3 cm); some up to 4.7 in (12 cm)

Key features Elongated body with rounded snout; deep-bodied exceptions include black widow tetra (*Gymnocorymbus ternetzi*) and silver tetra (*Tetragonopterus argenteus*); pointed teeth; generally large eyes, but 2 cave species are eyeless; fins well formed, dorsal larger and carries ray extensions in some males; adipose fin present, exception silvertip tetra (*Hasemania nana*); coloration variable, from pink in cave species to silvery to multicolored, e.g., cardinal tetra (*Paracheirodon axelrodi*); dark body and fin spots are common

Breeding Eggs scattered among vegetation, over the bottom, or over cracks and crevices; many species eat eggs; no parental protection of eggs or newborn; hatching starts at 1 day

Diet Smaller species feed on invertebrates and small aquatic creatures; larger ones feed on smaller fish; some feed on plants

Habitat Fresh water from creeks to lakes, river channels, and flooded forests; 2 species found exclusively in caves

Distribution From southern U.S. and Mexico to tropical and subtropical South America

Status Not threatened

Piranhas, Silver Dollars, and Pacus

The fearsome red-bellied piranha (*Pygocentrus nattereri*) of the Amazon and Orinoco basins grows up to 12 inches (30 cm) in length.

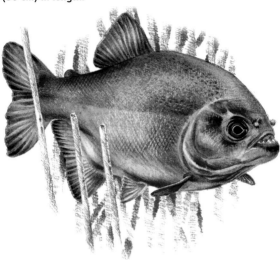

Common name Piranhas, silver dollars, and pacus

Subfamily Serrasalminae

Family Characidae

Order Characiformes

Number of species About 60 in 13 genera

Size From 6 in (15 cm) to 40 in (1 m)

Key features Body deep and compressed—pronounced in silver dollars; head blunt and massive; lower jaw protruding; sharp cutting teeth in piranhas, grinding teeth in nut and seed-eaters; fins well formed; coloration variable, from shiny and silvery to dull in the pacus and piranhas; some species attractively colored in chest area; fins may be distinctively colored

Breeding Several hundred or even thousand eggs from onset of wet season scattered or laid in prepared site; may or may not be guarded; spawning in pairs or shoals; hatching takes less than 1 week

Diet True piranhas feed on fish and other prey animals (reptiles, birds, and mammals), fruits, and seeds; silver dollars eat quantities of leaves; pacus mainly eat fruits and seeds; a few are specialized fin and scale eaters

Habitat From streams and clear water or blackwater rivers to turbid rivers, lakes, and flooded forests

Distribution Widespread in tropical South America

Status Not threatened

Croaking Tetras

The swordtail tetra (*Corynopoma riisei*) of Venezuela and Colombia feeds mainly at the surface on insects and larvae. Males develop long extensions on the lower lobe of their caudal fins. Length to 1.9 inches (4.8 cm).

Common name Croaking tetras

Subfamily Glandulocaudinae

Family Characidae

Number of species 50 in about 17 genera

Order Characiformes

Size From 0.7 in (1.8 cm) to 3.2 in (8 cm)

Key features Relatively compressed body, well-formed head; large eyes; mouth directed upward; well-formed, fine teeth; bristly mouthed tetras have nose and chin areas with tiny, bristlelike teeth; dorsal profile straight in most species; swordtail tetra (*Corynopoma riisei*) has deep chest and dorsal fin set well back, also large pectoral fins; males carry a distinctive gland (the caudal gland) at base of tail fin

Breeding Most are "normal" egg-scattering egg-layers; mating pairs press bodies close to enhance fertilization; a few species, e.g., swordtail tetra, have complex courtship and exhibit internal fertilization and incubation; male has long filaments extending from gill covers, each ending in fleshy tip (known as a paddle) that lures females and helps the pair align themselves for mating; when correctly aligned, male folds his anal fin toward female's genital opening and transfers sperm into female's body; eggs released shortly after fertilization and hatch in about 20–36 hours, depending on water temperature

Diet Predatory—insects in water or small aquatic invertebrates near the surface

Habitat Streams often with some current, close to water surface

Distribution South America

Status Not threatened

North American Freshwater Catfish

The channel catfish (*Ictalurus punctatus*) lives in rivers, large creeks, ponds, and reservoirs mainly in southern Canada and the east-central United States, although it has been introduced elsewhere. It is a popular sport and food fish. Length to 52 inches (1.3 m).

Common name North American freshwater catfish

Family Ictaluridae

Order Siluriformes

Number of species Around 45 in 7 genera

Size From 4 in (10 cm) long in madtoms and stonecat (*Noturus* spp.) to 19–65 in (48–165 cm) long in channel catfish (*Ictalurus* spp.)

Key features Body moderately elongated and scaleless; 4 pairs of barbels; teeth "velvety" pads (except toothless blindcat, *Trogloglanis pattersoni*—no teeth); stout spine at front of dorsal fin (except in *Prietella*); tail straight or round to moderately forked; adipose fin small and well separated from caudal in most species; in madtoms and stonecat it is long, low, and either joined or almost joined to caudal; madtoms and stonecat can produce venom; all species except widemouth blindcat (*Satan eurystomus*) and toothless blindcat have swim bladders; blindcats have no eyes

Breeding Nests saucer-shaped depressions or scrapings under overhangs, among vegetation, or in cavities; built by one or both spawners and vigorously defended; eggs: as few as 15 in madtoms and up to 10,000 in larger species; guarded by male, but female may play a role; hatching from 5–14 days depending on species and water temperature

Diet Aquatic invertebrates and other small fish; carrion may be taken

Habitat Rivers and lakes with sandy or muddy bottoms; some madtoms prefer fast-flowing waters; blind species prefer artesian wells

Distribution North and Central America from Hudson Bay and St. Lawrence drainages in Canada southward to the Rio Ucumacinta in Guatemala

Status IUCN lists 18 species under various levels of threat

Bagrid Catfish

The two-spot pink bagrid (*Mystus micracanthus*) is found in Sumatra, Java, Borneo, and Thailand, where it lives in shoals. It reaches 6 inches (15 cm) in length.

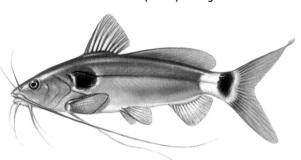

Common name Bagrid catfish

Family Bagridae

Order Siluriformes

Number of species Around 210 in 30 genera

Size From 3.2 in (8 cm) to 6.6 ft (2 m)

Key features Widely ranging characteristics; common features are a dorsal fin with a spine at the front; pectoral fins with a spine; adipose fin; complete lateral line in most species; minimum number of barbels: 3 pairs—some species also possess an additional pair of nasal barbels; 2 pairs of nostrils widely separated from each other, with one exception

Breeding Details only available for a few species, which care for their eggs and young; tawny dragon (*Pelteobagrus fluvidraco*) digs shallow nest in soft, fine-grained substrata during summer; male guards eggs until they hatch about 2 days later; at least 2 *Chrysichthys* species excavate caves in riverbanks and lay eggs inside that are guarded by both parents; in Guinea catfish (*Mystus tengara*) spawning often accompanied by chirping sounds

Diet Extremely varied; includes plant material, snails, other invertebrates, fish, and even human feces

Habitat Estuaries, lakes, rivers, streams, and pools occupied by family overall; most confined to fresh water

Distribution Widely found in Asia and Africa

Status IUCN lists 6 species under various levels of threat, including the clanwilliam rock-catfish (*Austroglanis gilli*) and *Pseudobagrus medianilis* as Critically Endangered

Sheatfish

The wels, or European catfish (*Silurus glanis*), is probably the best-known silurid; it is a fierce predator but very popular with anglers as a game and food fish. Length to 16.4 feet (5 m).

Common name Sheatfish

Family Siluridae

Order Siluriformes

Number of species Around 100 in 12 genera

Size From 1.8 in (4.5 cm) to maximum size of 16.4 ft (5 m)

Key features Body flattened from side to side from behind the head to the tail; 2 or 3 pairs of barbels, usually 2 on the lower jaw and 1 on the upper; lower jaw frequently slightly longer than the upper; short-based dorsal fin (7 rays or fewer) without a spine at the front; very long-based anal fin containing 41–110 rays; no adipose fin; pelvic fins sometimes absent

Breeding Depending on species, spawning takes place between June and August; nests may consist of depressions excavated by the male, which then guards the eggs until they hatch; some species undertake short migrations during floods

Diet Aquatic invertebrates, insects, and other fish; larger species also feed on amphibians, waterfowl, and aquatic mammals such as voles

Habitat Large lakes, rivers, and backwaters; many inhabit turbid waters with sandy or muddy substrata; glass catfish (*Kryptopterus* spp.) prefer clean midwater zones where they collect in shoals; wels (*Silurus glanis*) lives in brackish waters in the Baltic, Black, and Caspian Seas—deeper waters with little current preferred, spending most of the day hiding under roots and overhangs

Distribution Widely distributed in Asia; 2 species occur in Europe

Status IUCN lists 3 species as under threat, including the Endangered *Silurus mento*

Schilbeid Catfish

The 14-inch (35.5-cm) grass-cutter, butter, or striped catfish (*Schilbe mystus*), a species native to Africa that is bred for the aquarium and as a food fish.

Common name Schilbeid catfish

Family Schilbeidae (Schilbidae)

Order Siluriformes

Number of species Around 45 to 60 in around 18 genera

Size Range from 3.2 in (8 cm) to 19.7 in (50 cm)

Key features Extremely varied; most have a forked tail, a long or moderately long anal fin, and 4 pairs of barbels; some have translucent or almost-transparent bodies, with or without dorsal, adipose, or pelvic fins

Breeding Few details available; huge numbers of tiny eggs produced; no parental care is known to occur; spawning may involve migration during flood, then mating in shallow or swampy areas

Diet Primarily animal matter, from terrestrial insects and aquatic invertebrates to fish

Habitat Usually found in midwater; the butter catfish or grass-cutter close to the bottom; water often prone to seasonal flooding—at such times the catfish are found in shallow and swampy areas

Distribution Approximately 75 percent in tropical regions of Africa; the remainder mainly in southern Asia

Status Not threatened

Shark Catfish

The giant or Mekong catfish (*Pangasius gigas*) is a species native to the Mekong River system. A popular food fish, it can grow to 10 feet (3 m) in length.

Common name Shark catfish

Family Pangasiidae

Order Siluriformes

Number of species Around 25 in 2 genera

Size From 9 in (23 cm) to 10 ft (3 m)

Key features Elongated body; flattish head; soft skin; large eyes—set very low on head in giant catfish (*Pangasius gigas*); 2 to 3 pairs of barbels, often quite small, nasal barbels absent; well-formed dorsal fin with 1 prominent spine and 1 very small spine; small adipose fin; strong caudal fin; pectoral fins with prominent spine; anal fin contains 26–46 rays; young of iridescent shark (*P. hypophthalmus*) have 2 reflective bands running the length of body from behind the head to the tail

Breeding Many seasonal, though breeding season may vary even within the same species, depending on location; some are nonseasonal spawners

Diet Most have a wide-ranging diet that includes both animals and plants; the giant catfish is totally herbivorous

Habitat Large watercourses and lakes

Distribution Southern Asia from Borneo to Pakistan

Status IUCN lists giant catfish as Endangered mainly due to overfishing; captive-breeding programs have released thousands back into the wild

Asian Hillstream Catfish

The bottom-dwelling clown catfish (*Gagata cenia*) is about 6 inches (15 cm) long. One of the six species in its genus, it is found in India, Myanmar, and Thailand.

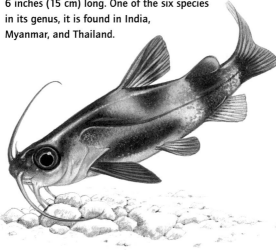

Common name Asian hillstream catfish

Family Sisoridae (Bagariidae)

Order Siluriformes

Number of species Around 100 in about 20 genera

Size From 0.8 in (2 cm) to around 8.2 ft (2.5 m)

Key features Generally flattened or conical head; 4 pairs of barbels (except the whiptail, *Sisor rhabdophorus*, which has 6 pairs); mouth underslung; dorsal fin with short base placed well forward, with the front edge in front of body midline; dorsal fin often carries a spine; adipose fin present; skin often quite thick and granular; chest and belly area flattened; may possess chest, belly, mouth, lip, or fin modifications for clinging to surfaces

Breeding No details available

Diet Most feed off encrusting algae and the microfauna they shelter; the giant river catfish (*Bagarius yarelli*) and closest relatives feed on prawns, invertebrates, and fish

Habitat Flowing waters in mountain rivers and streams, including torrents; usually found in areas with gravel, pebble, rock, or boulder substrata and at altitudes to over 4,900 ft (1,500 m)

Distribution Widely in southern Asia from Syria and Turkey eastward as far as southern China and Borneo

Status IUCN lists *Oreoglanis siamensis* as Vulnerable

Walking Catfish

The walking catfish (*Clarias batrachus*) is the best-known member of its family. It is found from India to Indonesia, but has also been introduced elsewhere. Length to 18.5 inches (47 cm).

Common name Walking catfish

Family Clariidae

Order Siluriformes

Number of species 100 in around 13 genera

Size From 4.7 in (12 cm) to around 4.6 ft (1.4 m)

Key features Elongated body, with some species eel-like; dorsal and anal fins long-based and lack a spine at the front—these fins may be joined to the caudal fin or may be separate; adipose fin usually absent; pectoral fins usually have spine (used in walking), but both pectoral and pelvic fins may be absent; body scaleless; head often flattened and covered in bony plates; eyes range from well formed to tiny or absent; mouth terminal (located at the tip of the snout) with 4 pairs of long barbels in most species (3 in some); modified gills and arborescent and superbranchial organs present in most genera to allow fish to breathe out of water

Breeding Usually at night, at beginning of rainy season, in shallow water; nesting possible but the eggs left unprotected once spawning completed; hatching around 23–30 hours

Diet From small aquatic insects and other invertebrates to fish and small birds

Habitat A wide range of freshwater habitats including lakes, pools, and backwaters; some live in caves or wells

Distribution Widely in Africa, parts of the Middle East, and southern and western Asia; as a food or aquarium fish in other regions—for example, Florida and Hawaii

Status IUCN lists 8 species under various levels of threat, including cave catfish (*Clarias cavernicola*), *C. maclareni*, *Encheloclarius curtisoma*, and *E. keliodes* as Critically Endangered

Airsac Catfish

Common name Airsac catfish (stinging, liver, or fossil catfish)

Scientific name *Heteropneustes fossilis* (including second species sometimes described as *H. microps*)

Family Heteropneustidae

Order Siluriformes

Size Up to 12 in (30 cm) long

Key features Elongated body; flattened head; 4 pairs of long barbels; short-based dorsal fin; pectoral fins with venomous spines; adipose fin missing or present as a low ridge; internally the fish possesses an elongated airsac extending back into the body from the gill chamber; if disturbed can be aggressive and use spines on pectoral fins to inflict a painful, sometimes fatal, sting on humans

Breeding Eggs laid in a depression prepared in shallow water by both parents; eggs and young defended by both adults; eggs take about 2 days to hatch; offspring guarded up to 1 month

Diet Wide-ranging—small fish, insects, and aquatic invertebrates

Habitat Mainly in slow-flowing or still waters, swamps, rice paddies, and ditches; often in turbid water

Distribution Widely in Bangladesh, India, Pakistan, Laos, Myanmar, Sri Lanka, Thailand, and possibly Nepal

Status Listed by IUCN as Vulnerable (under the name *H. microps*)

Frogmouth Catfish

The Indian frogmouth catfish (*Chaca chaca*), sometimes described as resembling a flattened leaf with a huge mouth at one end. Its tiny eyes help it avoid being spotted. Length to 7.8 inches (20 cm).

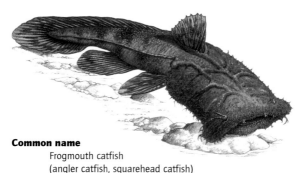

Common name
Frogmouth catfish
(angler catfish, squarehead catfish)

Family Chacidae

Order Siluriformes

Number of species 3 in 1 genus (*Chaca*)

Size Around 8 in (20 cm) long; some may grow bigger

Key features Flattened head; large, straight-edged, upward-pointing mouth; 3 or 4 pairs of barbels; very small eyes located on top of head; dorsal fin possesses stout, short serrated spine; pectoral fins possess a similar spine; adipose fin joined with caudal fin; body coloration mottled dark brown or blackish; can gulp large quantities of water through its mouth and force it out through narrow gill openings to create a form of "jet propulsion" for rapid movement

Breeding No details available

Diet Almost exclusively fish; unusual feeding technique to lure prey involves wiggling short maxillary barbels in a jerky movement to simulate movement of worms; enormous upturned mouth enables it to take in prey almost as big as itself

Habitat Slow-flowing or still waters with soft substrate; frequently mud

Distribution Bangladesh, Borneo, India, Indonesia, Malaysia, Myanmar, and Nepal

Status Not threatened

Electric Catfish

The electric catfish (*Malapterurus electricus*), a fierce 4-ft (1.2-m) predator widespread in tropical Africa. The electricity it produces is not only used to stun prey and deter predators but also to navigate and detect prey.

Common name Electric catfish

Family Malapteruridae

Order Siluriformes

Number of species 11 in 1 genus (*Malapterurus*)

Size From around 4.8 in (12.2 cm) to around 48 in (1.2 m)

Key features Sturdy head; small eyes; fleshy lips; 3 pairs of mouth barbels; nasal or "nose" barbels lacking; no dorsal fin; adipose fin well formed and located near the tail; rounded caudal fin; different degrees and intensity of mottling and body banding; electricity-producing organ beneath skin located from behind the head to just in front of adipose and anal fins; consists of specialized cells called electrocytes stacked on top of each other

Breeding May spawn in burrows excavated in river banks

Diet Smaller fish

Habitat Slow-moving or still waters containing rocks, sunken logs, and roots where the fish can shelter or rest in daylight hours; many preferred waters are tannin-stained (known as blackwaters) or turbid in nature

Distribution Widespread in tropical Africa from western Africa through central regions to the Nile River; individual species may have restricted ranges

Status Not threatened

Sea Catfish

The hardhead sea catfish (*Ariopsis felis*), a streamlined fish that lives along the west Atlantic coast. It feeds at night on crabs, shrimp, and small fish. Length to 28 inches (70 cm).

Common name Sea catfish (salmon catfish, shark catfish, fork-tailed catfish, crucifix fish)

Family Ariidae

Order Siluriformes

Number of species 120–150 in around 14 genera

Size From around 9.8 in (25 cm) to around 4.3 ft (1.8 m)

Key features Elongated with scaleless body; head usually depressed, flattened, or conically shaped with bony shield; 2 or 3 pairs of barbels present; dorsal and pectoral fins possess stout serrated spines that cause painful wounds; adipose fin present; caudal fin well forked

Breeding Some species are mouthbrooding—males take up fertilized eggs into their mouths and brood them orally for 4 weeks or longer; in mouthbrooding species females develop modifications on anal fin during breeding season; eggs often "marble-sized," almost 0.6 in (1.4 cm) in diameter

Diet Predatory, wide selection of prey animals and fish

Habitat Estuaries, coastal lagoons, and in coastal waters; some exclusively freshwater; many move between habitats; habitats contain sandy or muddy bottoms

Distribution Extremely wide in tropical and subtropical waters; may be found in temperate zones during summer

Status IUCN lists 8 species as under various levels of threat, including the New Grenada sea catfish (*Arius bonillai*), *A. festinus*, and *A. uncinatus* as Endangered

Tandan Catfish

The coral catfish (*Plotosus lineatus*) grows to about 12 inches (30 cm) and lives at the bottom of reefs and estuaries. In spite of its venomous spines, it is a popular aquarium fish.

Common name Tandan catfish (eeltail catfish, coral catfish, stinging catfish)

Family Plotosidae

Order Siluriformes

Number of species Around 32 in 9 genera

Size From around 4.8 in (12.2 cm) to about 35.4 in (90 cm)

Key features Elongate body, almost eel-like in some genera; flattened or rounded head; 4 pairs of barbels; dorsal and pectoral fins bear a serrated, venomous spine at the front; adipose fin absent; anal and caudal fin joined; top part of caudal fin extends forward along back as a caudodorsal fin with soft rays; tandan catfish stings have been known to cause extreme pain, swelling, and diarrhea in human victims

Breeding Little known generally; in dewfish (*Tandanus tandanus*) male digs large, circular nest up to 40 in (1 m) in diameter in sandy or muddy substrata of freshwater rivers or estuaries; male seeks out female and chases her to the nest, which may be filled with gravel, stones, or vegetation; female may lay over 20,000 eggs that are guarded by male; hatching takes 1 week, but male may guard site for up to 18 days; in coral catfish (*Plotosus lineatus*), a marine species, eggs may be laid during summer in a nest or rock crevice; nest and eggs protected by male; hatching takes 7–10 days

Diet Animal matter, including insects, snails, crustaceans, fish, and other invertebrates

Habitat Wide range, from coral reefs through estuaries to rivers; around 50 percent of species strictly freshwater

Distribution Indian Ocean and western Pacific Ocean extending from Japan to Australia

Status IUCN lists Kutubu tandan (*Oloplotosus torobo*) as Vulnerable

Upside-Down Catfish

The 4-inch (10-cm) upside-down catfish (*Synodontis nigriventris*) swims upside down to graze the underside of leaves for algae and tiny animals.

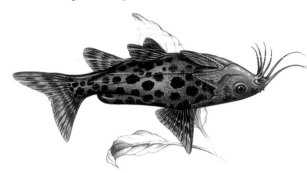

Common name Upside-down catfish (squeakers, squeaking catfish)

Family Mochokidae

Order Siluriformes

Number of species Around 170 in 10 genera

Size From around 2 in (5 cm) to around 27.5 in (70 cm)

Key features Normal-headed species have sloping forehead and slightly to moderately pointed snout; mouth on underside of tip of snout; in sucker-mouthed species mouth is broader and more straight-edged with fleshy lips and broad tooth pads; stout cephalic (head) shield found in all, extending to front of dorsal fin along the top and to the base of pectoral fins along the sides and bottom; 3 pairs of barbels (no nasal barbels), ornate in some; dorsal and pectoral fins possess a stout spine at front, can be "locked" in defense; adipose fin large, becoming sail like in normal-headed species

Breeding Few details available; eggs said to be adhesive and laid under cover; no parental care reported; hatching takes about 1 week; at least 2 species lay eggs among those laid by breeding mouthbrooding cichlids

Diet Small organisms, crustaceans, and plankton; algae scraped off rocks, logs, and submerged vegetation; larger species take small fish

Habitat Prefer slow-moving waters, lakes, and swamps; sucker-mouthed species prefer faster-flowing waters, some in torrents; many spend day hiding under submerged logs and roots or in caves and crevices

Distribution Widespread in most tropical regions of Africa including African Rift lakes

Status IUCN lists Incomati rock catlet (*Chiloglanis bifurcus*) as Critically Endangered

Talking Catfish

The dolphin catfish (*Pseudodoras niger*), a narrow-headed doradid, grows to 4 feet (1.2 m) but is a placid creature and eats tiny food particles.

Common name Talking catfish (thorny catfish)

Family Doradidae

Order Siluriformes

Number of species Around 80–100 in around 35 genera

Size From around 0.5 in (1.3 cm) to around 4 ft (1.2 m)

Key features Robust body; head largely covered by a cephalic (head) shield consisting of several bony plates; species divided into 2 groups depending on head shape; body with a row of hard thorny plates (scutes); most plates contain small, strong backward-pointing "thorns"; dorsal and pectoral fins have prominent, serrated (saw-edged) spine; when taken out of water, talking catfish continue opening and closing mouths in exaggerated manner and produce croaking sounds; sounds come from movement of pectoral fin spines or through body wall when swim bladder is vibrated; dolphin catfish (*Pseudodoras niger*) can raise dorsal and pectoral fin spines in defense and lock them in upright position for added protection

Breeding Very little known; most details relate to *Amblydoras hancocki,* which builds a nest of bubbles at the surface, defended by males

Diet Many doradids filter bottom sediments, feeding on small invertebrates and plant material; larger species feed on aquatic snails

Habitat Often found over soft substrata into which they can burrow; wide range of waters, including large rivers and flooded forests

Distribution Central and South America—primarily Brazil, Peru, and the Guianas

Status Not threatened

Driftwood Catfish

The driftwood catfish or common woodcat (*Trachelyopterus galeatus*) becomes increasingly dark with age. It gets its name because its coloration makes it resemble a piece of wood. The fish is widely distributed in the Amazon region from the northern tip of South America to tropical Peru. Length to 8.7 inches (22 cm).

Common name Driftwood catfish (woodcats)

Family Auchenipteridae

Order Siluriformes

Number of species About 65–75 in 21 genera

Size Most about 6 in (15 cm) in length or less, some barbelless species around 21.7 in (55 cm)

Key features Head may be flattened; has stout, bony plates (cephalic or nuchal shield) that extend to front edge of dorsal fin; usually 3 pairs of barbels, with maxillary ones fitting into groove under eye; barbelless species (sometimes classified as a separate family: the Ageneiosidae) have 1 pair of short barbels; body scaleless; lateral line organ has rough zig-zag or irregular pattern; dorsal and pectoral fins have prominent spine at front; adipose fin small or lacking; well formed caudal, anal, and pectoral fins

Breeding Internal fertilization typical, several hundred eggs laid

Diet Predatory; feed on smaller fish and insects

Habitat Mostly nocturnal, spending day resting in holes in wood or rocks, in slow-flowing habitats; some, like ageneiosids, found in midwater in large rivers

Distribution South America from Panama southward to Argentina

Status Not threatened

Antenna Catfish

The red-tailed catfish (*Phractocephalus hemioliopterus*) has been a victim of commercial overexploitation, and numbers are dwindling. Although extremely predatory, this beautiful fish is a great favorite with enthusiasts and collectors. It is found in the wild in Peru, Brazil, Guyana, and Venezuela. Length to 53 inches (134 cm).

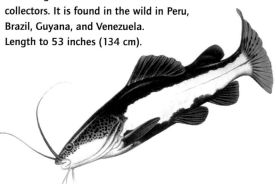

Common name Antenna catfish (long-whiskered catfish)

Family Pimelodidae

Order Siluriformes

Number of species Around 300 in 56 genera

Size From 3.2 in (8 cm) to 10 feet (3 m)

Key features Body form and coloration very diverse; general features: elongated scaleless body; 3 pairs of long barbels (nasal barbels absent); terminal (or almost terminal) mouth in all but 2 species; adipose fin and forked caudal fin present in all species except one; well-formed eyes except for a few cave species that are eyeless

Breeding No documented accounts currently available

Diet Fish; carrion; human waste; larger species may eat other animals such as small monkeys

Habitat Most prefer the bottom zone of flowing waters; a few inhabit caves or subterranean watercourses

Distribution Widely in central and South America extending northward to the southernmost regions of Mexico

Status IUCN lists 4 species as under various levels of threat

Whale Catfish

The whale catfish *Pseudocetopsis gobiodes* grows to about 6 inches (15 cm) in length. It is found in Brazil, Paraguay, and Argentina, but like many other whale catfish its biology is little known.

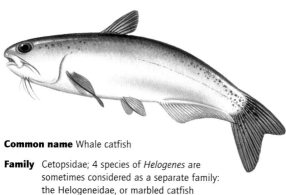

Common name Whale catfish

Family Cetopsidae; 4 species of *Helogenes* are sometimes considered as a separate family: the Helogeneidae, or marbled catfish

Order Siluriformes

Number of species Around 12–23 in 4–7 genera according to classification system used

Size Range from about 0.7 in (1.8 cm) to about 10.4 in (26.4 cm)

Key features Usually large, rounded head with small eyes; powerful jaws armed with numerous small teeth, located slightly under tip of snout; body smooth with no scales; 3 pairs of barbels (no nasal barbels); adipose fin absent (except in some *Helogenes*, where presence or absence can vary within a single species); reduced swim bladder

Breeding Habits are unknown

Diet Exclusively carnivorous: large fish and mammals; strong teeth allow them to open up large holes in body of prey and slip inside to feed

Habitat Mostly in turbid waters and along sandy and muddy bottoms of rivers

Distribution Tropical South America

Status Not threatened

Banjo Catfish

The 4.7-inch (12-cm) long banjo catfish (*Bunocephalus coracoideus*) lies buried in silt, where its excellent camouflage helps conceal it. The species is also called the frying pan catfish.

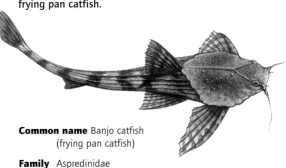

Common name Banjo catfish (frying pan catfish)

Family Aspredinidae

Order Siluriformes

Number of species Around 29 in 12 genera

Size Most under 6 in (15 cm); largest can grow to 16.5 in (42 cm)

Key features Head and anterior part of body flattened and much broader than the rest of body; posterior half of body narrow and elongated; body scaleless, containing numerous tubercles; gill openings reduced to slits; adipose fin lacking; anal fin has 50–60 rays in the Aspredininae, 5–18 rays in the Bunocephalinae

Breeding Information scarce; reports refer to several thousand eggs being laid by some species of Bunocephalinae, such as the frying pan catfish (*Bunocephalus coracoideus*), in a depression excavated by male; eggs are protected by male; in Aspredininae the eggs become attached to the abdomen of the female via a thin stalk containing blood vessels; developing embryos possibly receive food by this route; similar arrangement reported in sea catfish (family Ariidae) that inhabit similar estuarine habitats

Diet Mainly bottom-dwelling invertebrates, especially worms

Habitat Bunocephalinae generally found in shaded waters close to water currents, on fine-grained substratum with some leaf litter; Aspredininae found closer to coasts, in muddy brackish or marine waters; Hoplomyzontinae strictly freshwater species preferring vegetated waters

Distribution Widespread in tropical South America

Status Not threatened

Parasitic Catfish

The parasitic candirú (*Vandellia cirrhosa*) is only 1 inch (2.5 cm) long. It lives in rivers and streams in the Amazon basin.

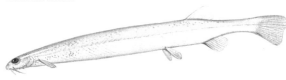

Common name Parasitic catfish (pencil catfish, spiny-headed catfish)

Family Trichomycteridae (Pygidiidae)

Order Siluriformes

Number of species Around 155 in 36 genera

Size From 0.8 in (2 cm) to around 6 in (15 cm)

Key features Elongate, some species eel-like—particularly parasitic types; some free-living species resemble loaches (family Cobitidae); number of barbels vary: at least 2 pairs; most species possess pelvic fins, but absent in at least 6 genera; gill covers carry spines

Breeding No details available

Diet Small invertebrates; parasitic types (which are, in fact, the minority of the family) feed on blood or on scales and body mucus of other fish; the candirú (*Vandellia cirrhosa*) senses minute current of water produced by gill plates of a potential victim and swims toward it; as the victim opens gill plate, the candirú dives into the gill chamber, attaches itself to the gills, rasps away the delicate tissue, and drinks blood that oozes from the wound created; 1 recorded case of candirú entering human urinary tract

Habitat Predominantly bottom dwellers; parasitic types and a few others, such as *Tridentopsis*, frequent midwater levels more regularly; some prefer clear, cool, flowing waters

Distribution Widely distributed in South America

Status IUCN lists 11 species as under various levels of threat, including *Rhizosomichthys totae* from Lake Tota, Colombia, as Extinct

Armored Catfish

The slender armored catfish (*Callichthys callichthys*) is immediately recognizable by its unusual, plated scales. This species often forms shoals and is common in South America. Length to 6.5 inches (16.5 cm).

Common name Armored catfish (callichthyid armored catfish)

Family Callichthyidae

Order Siluriformes

Number of species 208 in 8 genera

Size From around 1.25 in (3 cm) to 8.8 in (22 cm)

Key features All callichthyids have 2 rows of overlapping bony plates on body; up to 2 pairs of well-developed barbels and fleshy flaps or other extensions on lower lip; in Callichthyinae snout more or less depressed (flattened from top to bottom); mouth on underside of snout; in addition to barbels around the mouth a pair of threadlike outgrowths on upper jaw and fleshy flaps on lower lip; in Corydoradinae snout rounded or compressed (flattened from side to side); small mouth under tip of snout; no threadlike processes present on upper jaw

Breeding Callichthyinae build bubble nests for eggs that are guarded by male; Corydoradinae fertilize eggs uniquely: female "drinks" in sperm released by male then expels it from her vent before funneling it into her pelvic fin pouch; seconds later, eggs are released; eggs abandoned after laying; eggs hatch in 3–4 days in both subfamilies

Diet Wide range of invertebrates and plant debris

Habitat Fast-flowing to still waters; most are bottom-hugging species, but there are a few exceptions

Distribution Tropical regions of South America

Status Not threatened

Suckermouth Armored Catfish

The spotted pleco (*Hypostomus punctatus*) is found in the
lower reaches of rivers in and around Guyana.
It grows to 12 inches (30 cm).

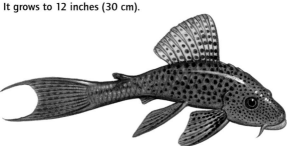

Common name Suckermouth armored catfish

Family Loricariidae

Order Siluriformes

Number of species Around 550–600 in around 80 genera

Size From under 2 in (5 cm) to 20–24 in (50–60 cm) or more
in some plecos

Key features Fairly flattened or sloping head, often adorned
with bristles in males; underslung, suckerlike mouth with
pads containing numerous tiny scraping teeth; eyes
possess a light-regulating flap; 3 pairs of barbels; body
covered in overlapping bony plates (scutes); "chin" and
lower surface of body flat; caudal fin usually well
formed; dorsal, pectoral, and pelvic fins usually carry a
stout spine

Breeding Eggs laid in open, under shelter, or in burrows
according to species

Diet Most species feed on encrusting algae and detritus,
together with attendant creatures such as small
crustaceans and aquatic insects; also feed on carrion

Habitat From lowland still waters to fast-flowing streams
in the highlands

Distribution Widely in Central and tropical South America

Status Not threatened

Pikes and Pickerels

At 6 feet (1.8 m) in length, the muskellunge (*Esox masquinongy*) is the longest member of the family Esocidae. This huge North American freshwater predator feeds on a variety of other animals, including fish, ducklings, aquatic mammals such as muskrats, and snakes.

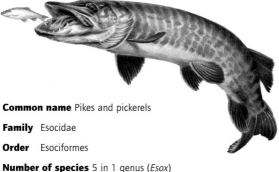

Common name Pikes and pickerels

Family Esocidae

Order Esociformes

Number of species 5 in 1 genus (*Esox*)

Size From around 15.5 in (39.5 cm) to about 6 ft (1.8 m)

Key features Elongated body; large, pointed head with distinct duck-billed snout; large mouth with numerous pointed teeth; lower jaw slightly longer than upper; eyes in top half of head; all fins well formed; no adipose fin; pectoral fins close to gill openings; dorsal and anal fins set well back along body; caudal fin forked; body often mottled with irregular streaks; pale belly

Breeding Usually in spring; males arrive at breeding sites before females; cool, shallow waters preferred, underwater vegetation essential; spawning can occur in groups of 1 female and 2 or 3 males; eggs and sperm scattered among vegetation and spread out over several weeks; large female can release up to 600,000 sticky eggs; no parental protection; hatching takes a few days to nearly a month depending on water temperature

Diet Small fish, insects, and other invertebrates during juvenile stages; larger pikes eat amphibians, larger fish, crayfish, small mammals, waterfowl

Habitat Predominantly fresh water but also in brackish conditions; slow-flowing or still waters preferred, especially heavily vegetated and shallow; can be found at 100 ft (30 m); cool water temperatures preferred but not restricted to such conditions

Distribution Widely distributed in Northern Hemisphere but not naturally occurring in northern Norway or northern Scotland

Status Not threatened

Mudminnows

The 13-inch (33-cm) Alaska blackfish (*Dallia pectoralis*) is the largest species of mudminnow. It is found in heavily vegetated swamps and ponds, and occasionally rivers and lakes from Alaska into the Yukon, the Bering Sea islands, and northeastern Siberia.

Common name Mudminnows

Family Umbridae

Order Esociformes

Number of species 5 in 3 genera

Size From 3.2 in (8 cm) to 13 in (33 cm)

Key features Elongated, stocky body; head usually with blunt snout; eyes medium-sized; all fins well formed; adipose fin absent; dorsal and anal fins located in rear half of body (closer to midline in *Umbra* than other genera); caudal fin rounded; caudal peduncle deep; mottled in most species; but Alaska blackfish (*Dallia pectoralis*) is dark green or brown above, fading to light colors with mottling on lower half of body

Breeding Eggs usually laid in shallow depression; female European mudminnow (*Umbra krameri*) defends her 100 to 120 eggs until they hatch after a few days; both males and females die after spawning in this species; no reports of either nest building or egg protection available for Alaska blackfish, in which up to 300 eggs are laid over a period of days following an upriver migration

Diet Mainly invertebrates; some species take small fish

Habitat Slow-moving or standing fresh waters, usually with abundant vegetation and over fine-grained or muddy bottom; ponds and swamps can experience low water and oxygen levels during hot season; central mudminnow (*U. limi*) burrows into mud and goes into a period of summer sleep

Distribution Northern Hemisphere for family as a whole; individual species can be more restricted: e.g., European mudminnow confined to eastern Europe, Alaska blackfish in Alaska and Siberia

Status IUCN lists European mudminnow as Vulnerable and Olympic mudminnow (*Novumbra hubbsi*) as Lower Risk

Argentines

The 28-inch (70-cm) greater argentine (*Argentina silus*) is found at depths of between 140 and 1,440 feet (43–439 m) in the eastern and western Atlantic.

Common name Argentines (herring smelts)

Family Argentinidae

Order Osmeriformes

Number of species About 25 in 2 genera (*Argentina, Glossanodon*

Size From 3.2 in (8 cm) to around 27.5 in (70 cm)

Key features Elongated body; pointed snout; large eyes; all fins well formed; dorsal fin slightly in front of pelvic fins; adipose fin present in line with anal fin and set well back on body; caudal fin distinctly forked; silvery sides and lower half of body, dark above

Breeding Eggs and sperm scattered in open water in winter and spring, then abandoned; greater argentine (*A. silus*) breeds in deep water to a depth of 1,300 to 1,400 ft (400–500 m)

Diet Predominantly invertebrates such as crustaceans, worms, squids, and comb jellies (some species); larger individuals and species also take fish

Habitat Almost exclusively marine; wide range of depths: e.g., North Pacific argentine (*A. sialis*) found in both brackish estuaries and open sea from 36 ft (11 m) to 820–900 ft (250–275 m); greater argentine to 4,725 ft (1,440 m)

Distribution Tropical and subtropical regions of Atlantic, Indian, and Pacific Oceans

Status Not threatened

Barreleyes

The 3.2-inch (8-cm) mirrorbelly (*Opisthoproctus grimaldii*) has a depth range between 985 and 6,560 feet (300–2,000 m). It occurs in tropical and subtropical regions of the Atlantic and western Pacific. The dorsal part of its head is transparent.

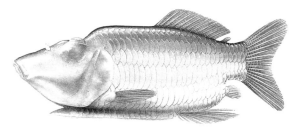

Common name Barreleyes (spookfish)

Family Opisthoproctidae

Order Osmeriformes

Number of species 11 in 6 genera

Size From 1.7 in (4.4 cm) to around 20 in (50 cm)

Key features Extremely elongated to stocky body; pointed snout; skull almost transparent in some species (e.g., mirrorbelly, *Opisthoproctus grimaldii*); large eyes, usually tubular, directed upward or forward; adipose fin present in some species; pelvic fins almost winglike to much smaller and "normal"; flat, oval, solelike belly (mirrorbelly and barreleye, *O. soleatus*); photophores (light organs) present near anus in some species, around eyes in others (brownsnout spookfish, *Dolichopteryx longipes*); usually dark to black, but silvery in mirrorbelly

Breeding Breeding habits unknown, but eggs and larvae are planktonic or pelagic (found at surface or midwater)

Diet Invertebrates, mainly crustaceans and copepods; mirrorbelly feeds on jellyfish and their relatives

Habitat Marine waters from near the surface at nighttime and only in some species (barreleye) down to around 8,200 ft (2,500 m) in other species; limits of habitat determined by temperature and salt content of water

Distribution Tropical and temperate regions of Atlantic, Indian, and Pacific Oceans

Status Not threatened

Smelts

The flesh of the 10-inch (25-cm) ayu (*Plecoglossus altivelis altivelis*) is highly esteemed, giving it the alternative name of sweetfish. It occurs widely in the northwest Pacific of China, Korea, and Japan.

Common name Smelts

Families Osmeridae (smelts), Plecoglossidae (ayus)

Order Osmeriformes

Number of species Osmeridae: 15 in 6 genera; Plecoglossidae: 1 in 1 genus

Size From around 4.5 in (11.5 cm) to 27.6 in (70 cm)

Key features Elongated body; pointed snout; large mouth; unique, leaflike, loosely attached teeth in ayu (*Plecoglossus altivelis altivelis*); upper jaw may extend beyond eye; dorsal fin placed centrally along the back; adipose fin present; forked caudal fin; anal fin set well back along body, its leading edge in front of adipose fin; pelvic fins on belly with front edge slightly behind dorsal fin; pectoral fins immediately behind and below gill covers; easily detached scales; dark back, often bluish-green, silvery sides, and white belly; fins often dark; ayu: orange patch behind head, yellowish fins; delta smelt (*Hypomesuus transpacificus*): black streak on dorsal fin and dark adipose fin

Breeding Eggs sticky, usually deposited in gravel; spawning in fresh water or the sea (in shallow water or on beaches); ayu lays eggs in shallow pit; some eggs have short stalk that breaks off, releasing eggs into water; hatching takes several weeks; young born in fresh water can drift out to sea; up to 50,000 eggs can be laid, usually fewer

Diet Predominantly insects and crustaceans; also some species take algae, squid, fish, or jellyfish

Habitat Wide-ranging: some marine species from surface down to 985 ft (300 m); many species spawn in fresh water but spend at least one winter at sea; some migrating species travel great distances up river; some species have landlocked populations; pygmy smelt (*Osmerus spectrum*) restricted to fresh water; a few spend time in fresh water and brackish estuaries

Distribution Northern Hemisphere in Atlantic and Pacific Oceans; ayus in China, Japan, and Korea

Status IUCN lists delta smelt and Ryukyu ayu-fish (*P. a. ryukyuensis*) as Endangered; pygmy smelt and European smelt (*O. eperlanus*) listed as Data Deficient

Noodlefish

The 3.6-inch (9.2-cm) Japanese icefish (*Salangichthys microdon*) occurs in the marine waters of the northwest Pacific from eastern Siberia and Russia to Japan and Korea, but it can also enter the fresh and brackish waters of rivers and estuaries.

Common name Noodlefish

Families Salangidae (noodlefish or icefish), Sundasalangidae (Sundaland noodlefish)

Order Osmeriformes

Number of species Salangidae: about 20 in 6 genera; Sundasalangidae: 7 in 1 genus

Size From around 1 in (2.5 cm) to 6.7 in (17 cm)

Key features Elongated, very slender body; head pointed but depressed in noodlefish; well-formed eyes; deepest part of body usually closer to tail than to front; dorsal and anal fins on posterior half of body; adipose fin present in icefish, absent in Sundaland noodlefish; tail forked; body scaleless except for 1 row of scales above anal fin base in male noodlefish; no rays in pectoral fins in Sundaland noodlefish; body transparent but translucent in some icefish

Breeding No information available; adults are neotenic (can breed but still retain some larval characteristics); some species spawn in spring

Diet Insects, crustaceans, and possibly other aquatic invertebrates

Habitat Some noodlefish and Sundaland noodlefish confined to fresh water, others migrate between fresh water and sea; most found in flowing waters

Distribution Asia, including China, Japan, Korea, Sakhalin (Russia), Vietnam, Borneo, and southern Thailand

Status IUCN lists ariakehimeshirauo (*Neosalanx regani*) as Vulnerable

Galaxiids

The 4.5-inch (11.5-cm) Murray jollytail (*Galaxias rostratus*) is found in Australia's Murray River system, which has tributaries in South Australia, Victoria, and New South Wales. It inhabits stream edges over rocky or sandy bottoms, sometimes among vegetation, and feeds on aquatic insects and crustaceans.

Common name Galaxiids

Subfamilies Aplochitoninae, Galaxiinae, Lovettiinae

Family Galaxiidae

Order Osmeriformes

Number of species Aplochitoninae: 2 in 2 genera; Galaxiinae: about 47 in 5 genera; Lovettiinae:1 in 1 genus

Size From around 1.6 in (4 cm) to about 13.2 in (33.5 cm)

Key features Elongated, scaleless body, tubular in cross-section, lateral line present; snout pointed in Aplochitoninae, blunter in Galaxiinae; eyes vary in size; dorsal and anal fins set well back along body in Galaxiinae, dorsal fin much farther forward in Aplochitoninae; adipose fin present in Aplochitoninae, absent in Galaxiinae; caudal fin distinctly forked in Aplochitoninae, slightly forked, straight-edged, or rounded in Galaxiinae

Breeding Eggs scattered in winter or spring, then abandoned in most species

Diet Aquatic insects and other invertebrates; also terrestrial or aerial insects that fall into the water

Habitat Fast-flowing streams to slow-moving, standing waters; some juveniles spend some time at sea

Distribution Australia, New Zealand, New Caledonia, and southern regions of Africa and South America

Status IUCN lists 23 species as under various levels of threat, including the swan galaxias (*Galaxias fontanus*), barred galaxias (*G. fuscus*), Clarence galaxias (*G. johnstoni*), and pedder galaxias (*G. pedderensis*) as Critically Endangered

Whitefish and Ciscoes

The 29-inch (73-cm) common whitefish (*Coregonus lavaretus*) occurred only in lakes within the Rhone River basin. Now it is stocked in many other places in Europe outside its native range.

Common name Whitefish and ciscoes (inconnu)

Scientific names *Coregonus, Prosopium, Stenodus*

Subfamily Coregoninae

Family Salmonidae

Order Salmoniformes

Number of species 72 in 3 genera

Size From around 6.3 in (16 cm) to 4.9 ft (1.5 m)

Key features Elongated body; head pointed to varying degrees; snout can be broad, pinched, or more pointed; mouth small or large with lower jaw longer than the upper; weak or no teeth to numerous teeth; 1 flap of skin between nostril in *Prosopium*, 2 in others; large eyes set in top half of head, exceptionally large in *P. coulteri*; lump behind head in one species; all fins well formed; dorsal fin in line with pelvic fins or nearly so; anal fin set well back on body in line with adipose fin; tail forked in all species; varying dark shades along back; silvery or whitish sides

Breeding All egg scatterers; many spawn after migrations upriver either from sea or lakes and rivers; eggs can take months to hatch; depending on species young move downstream, into estuaries, or the sea; landlocked populations remain in lakes

Diet Invertebrates ranging from plankton to insects; also mollusks, crustaceans, and some fish

Habitat Well-oxygenated, moving waters preferred; lake populations prefer slow-flowing and still conditions

Distribution Widely distributed in Northern Hemisphere; some species have very restricted distribution: e.g., Bear Lake whitefish (*P. gemmifer*) occur only in Bear Lake between southwestern Idaho and northern Utah

Status IUCN lists 15 species of *Coregonus* and 1 of *Stenodus* as under various levels of threat, including longjaw cisco (*C. alpenae*), deepwater cisco (*C. johannae*), and blackfin cisco (*C. nigripinnis*) as Extinct

Graylings

The 24-inch (61-cm) European grayling (*Thymallus thymallus*) occurs in Britain and France east to the Ural Mountains in northwest Russia. It inhabits well-oxygenated waters and feeds on insects, nymphs, small worms, and crustaceans.

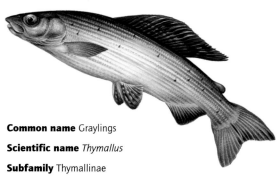

Common name Graylings

Scientific name *Thymallus*

Subfamily Thymallinae

Family Salmonidae

Order Salmoniformes

Number of species 5 (with 1 containing 4 subspecies) in 1 genus

Size From around 7.9 in (20 cm) to about 30 cm (76 cm)

Key features Elongated body, slightly compressed, with deepest point around the "shoulder"; small, sloping head, pointed snout; mouth small and slightly below tip of snout; numerous small teeth on both jaws; medium to largish eyes on top half of head; all fins well formed; dorsal fin sail-like, especially in males, front edge about halfway between line of pectoral and pelvic fins; anal fin set well back in line with adipose fin; caudal fin large and distinctly forked; scales moderately large; dark color on back, fading to silvery along sides and belly; numerous dark spots on body and dorsal fin; color more vivid in males

Breeding In spring female excavates shallow depression (redd) usually in shallow water with sandy or gravelly bottom; male wraps dorsal fin over female's back during spawning; 8,000 or more eggs are buried, hatching out after 3–4 weeks

Diet Mainly bottom-living invertebrates; also feeds from surface, taking flying insects that fall into the water

Habitat Flowing, middle reaches of rivers—the "Grayling Zone"; clear, well-oxygenated water with gravelly or sandy bottom, or riffles between pools

Distribution Widely distributed in Northern Hemisphere; narrower distribution in some species

Status Not threatened

Char

The 34-inch (86-cm) brook char (*Salvelinus fontinalis*) occurs widely in clear, cool, well-oxygenated creeks, small to medium rivers, and lakes in eastern parts of North America.

Common name Char

Scientific names *Salvelinus, Salvethymus*

Subfamily Salmoninae

Family Salmonidae

Order Salmoniformes

Number of species 39 in 2 genera

Size From around 9.5 in (24 cm) to around 4.9 ft (1.5 m)

Key features Streamlined body; rounded to pointed snout with rounded tip; large mouth; teeth on both jaws; eyes moderate to large; all fins well formed; dorsal has fewer than 16 rays, lacks spines; adipose fin present; caudal fin slightly forked or almost straight-edged; anal fin set well back on body; pelvic fins on belly; pectoral fins behind and below gill covers; minute scales; variable coloration; typical spotted body; dark back and top of sides, lighter lower sides and belly; white front edge on anal and pelvic fins

Breeding Anadromous species and populations migrate from the sea into rivers to spawn; landlocked (lake-dwelling) species and populations migrate into nearby rivers or remain in lake to search out gravelly areas; males establish territories, which females enter to excavate shallow depression (redd); pair release eggs and sperm in the redd; eggs take up to 70 days to hatch; adults return to sea or lake after spawning

Diet Invertebrates from plankton, sponges, worms, and crustaceans to aquatic and terrestrial insects; also fish, amphibians, and small mammals

Habitat Some species spend most of year at sea; migrate into fresh water to spawn; landlocked species in cool, flowing stretches, pools, and lakes

Distribution Northern Hemisphere; some species wide-ranging, others restricted

Status IUCN lists 1 species as Endangered, 2 (including *Salvethymus*) Vulnerable, 1 Extinct

Huchen or Danube Salmon

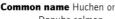

Common name Huchen or Danube salmon (hunchen, European river trout, Danube trout)

Scientific name *Hucho hucho*

Subfamily Salmoninae

Family Salmonidae

Order Salmoniformes

Size Around 4.9 ft (1.5 m) but reported up to 6.5 ft (2 m)

Key features Elongated, cigar-shaped body; large head; broad mouth with numerous teeth; back edge extends beyond eye; eyes close to top of head; all fins well formed; dorsal fin in front of pelvic fins; anal fin set well back along body in line with adipose fin; powerful forked tail; scales very small; dark greenish on back, silvery sides with a pink sheen, white belly; numerous small X-shaped dark spots on body

Breeding Early to midspring over gravelly beds in fast-flowing water; female excavates shallow depression (redd), in which she lays and buries her eggs; hatching takes up to 5 weeks; no parental protection

Diet Juveniles feed on invertebrates; adults feed almost exclusively on fish; also amphibians, reptiles, mammals, and waterfowl

Habitat Prefers tributaries of large, well-oxygenated, fast-flowing rivers but also found in backwaters

Distribution Native to the Danube River basin

Status Listed by IUCN as Endangered mainly due to pollution, overfishing, draining of habitat, damming of rivers, and excessive removal of water for industry and agriculture

Atlantic Salmon

Common name Atlantic salmon (salmon and many other names)

Scientific name *Salmo salar*

Subfamily Salmoninae

Family Salmonidae

Order Salmoniformes

Size Extremely variable at maturity but up to 4.9 ft (1.5 m)

Key features Elongated body; pointed snout with rounded tip; large mouth; numerous teeth in both jaws; dorsal fin slightly in front of pelvic fin line; adipose fin present; tail slightly forked; anal fin slightly in front of adipose fin line; pelvic fins on belly; scales very small; fish returning from sea predominantly silver with darker back and white belly; pectoral fins relatively low and behind gill covers; sides have small, X-shaped spots; male's jaw becomes hooked (a kype)

Breeding In fresh water usually between October and January in flowing streams with gravelly bottoms; female excavates nests (redds); eggs covered, then abandoned; adults return to sea or home lake; most oceangoing adults die before entering sea, but some (mostly females) survive; eggs hatch after several months

Diet Young fish eat plankton and small invertebrates, then larger invertebrates; oceangoing adults' diet is squid, shrimp, and fish; landlocked adults eat freshwater crustaceans and fish

Habitat Open sea close to coasts during prespawning phase in migrating populations; deep pools and river stretches in landlocked populations; clear, oxygen-rich, flowing waters preferred by latter; same conditions required for spawning; shallow water preferred by all populations

Distribution Both sides of northern Atlantic Ocean; in the west from northern Quebec in Canada to Connecticut; in the east from Arctic Circle to Portugal, southern Greenland and Iceland to Barents Sea; introduced into many locations, including Australia, New Zealand, Argentina, Chile; some introductions not established

Status Not threatened

Sockeye Salmon

Common name Sockeye salmon (red salmon, kokanee, and many others)

Scientific name *Oncorhynchus nerka*

Subfamily Salmoninae

Family Salmonidae

Order Salmoniformes

Size Wide range of sizes at maturity: from around 16 in (40 cm) to about 33 in (84 cm)

Key features Elongated body; moderately pointed snout with rounded tip; large mouth extending beyond eye in large specimens; teeth on both jaws; eyes relatively small; all fins well formed; back edge of dorsal fin in line with front edge of pelvic fins; adipose fin present; tail slightly forked; anal fin in front of line of adipose fin; pelvic fins on belly; pectoral fins behind and below gill covers; tiny scales; sea-based stocks are blue-black along back with silvery belly; small black specks along back and caudal fin; body becomes brilliant red during breeding season in both males and females; fins (except caudal and pectorals) also become red, head becomes green; male's jaw develops into a pronounced hook (kype) during breeding season

Breeding Fresh water: shallow, flowing, oxygen-rich streams with gravelly bottoms; some spawn along lake or island shores at depths of 7–10 ft (2.3 m), occasionally down to 100 ft (30 m); female excavates redd; female covers eggs as she digs a new redd at front edge of the one in which she has laid her eggs; all adults die after spawning; hatching takes 6 weeks to 5 months; landlocked stocks (kokanee) remain in fresh water

Diet Young fish eat plankton, then small fish and larger invertebrates; sockeye eat larger fish during oceangoing stages; kokanee eat invertebrates

Habitat Mature in open sea at depths of up to 820 ft (250 m); landlocked populations in lakes

Distribution Both coasts of Pacific; in the east from Alaska down to California; in the west around Japan and Russia; introduced to several countries

Status Not threatened

Sea, Brown, Brook, Lake Trout

Common name Sea, brown, brook, lake trout

Scientific name *Salmo trutta*

Subfamily Salmoninae

Family Salmonidae

Order Salmoniformes

Size From about 9.4 in (24 cm) to about 4.6 ft (1.4 m)

Key features Elongated body; pointed snout with rounded to blunt tip; large mouth, upper jaw extending beyond eye; dorsal fin in front of line of pelvic fins; adipose fin present; tail almost straight-edged; anal fin almost in line with adipose fin; pelvic fins on belly, closer to anal than pectoral fins; pectoral fins right behind and below gill covers; variable coloration: estuary and sea-living populations have few dark body spots; freshwater populations heavily spotted; almost black or brown along back, fading to orange down sides and yellowish or whitish along belly; body spots predominantly very dark with fewer rusty-red spots

Breeding In fresh water usually between October and January; no large-scale migration; most adults survive breeding season to spawn again

Diet Mostly aquatic insects, crustaceans, and aerial insects; larger specimens eat fish, plus snails, tadpoles, frogs, toads, newts, and salamanders

Habitat Sea trout (*Salmo trutta trutta*), brown trout (*S. t. fario*), and *S. t. macrostigma* spend time at sea, return to fresh water to spawn; Aral trout (*S. t. aralensis*), Amu-Darya trout (*S. t. oxianus*), and lake trout (*S. t. lacustris*) restricted to fresh water; well-oxygenated, clear, flowing waters preferred by all types; sea trout remain in top 33 ft (10 m), *S. t. macrostigma* descend to depths of 3,300–8,200 ft (1,000–2,500 m); in rivers and lakes, preferring sheltered locations in shallow, flowing water

Distribution Eurasia; also introduced into many countries

Status IUCN lists Aral trout as Critically Endangered

Rainbow Trout

Common name Rainbow trout (steelhead, plus many others)

Scientific name *Oncorhynchus mykiss*

Subfamily Salmoninae

Family Salmonidae

Order Salmoniformes

Size Nearly 4 ft (1.2 m) maximum; some populations, especially some landlocked ones, smaller and lighter

Key features Elongated body; pointed snout with rounded to blunt tip; large mouth, upper jaw extending beyond eye in large specimens; teeth in both jaws; older males have hooked lower jaw; dorsal fin almost in line with pelvic fins; adipose fin present; tail slightly forked; back edge of anal fin almost in line with adipose fin; pelvic fins on belly, closer to anal than to pectoral fins; pectoral fins immediately behind and below gill covers; variable coloration: steelheads steel-gray and silvery during oceangoing phase, changing to rainbow coloring in fresh water; pinkish "rainbow" band runs from cheeks to caudal peduncle; numerous black spots along bluish-black back and down sides

Breeding Behavior like other trout and salmon; breeding season largely depends on location; egg laying occurs during December in south, as late as May or June in far north; eggs hatch after 1 month depending on temperature

Diet Wide range of aquatic invertebrates and aerial insects; larger specimens also take fish

Habitat Landlocked and other exclusively freshwater populations (rainbows) tolerate conditions from fast-flowing, oxygen-rich streams to still lakes; oceangoing populations (steelheads) travel hundreds of miles out to sea but remain in top 655 ft (209 m) of water column

Distribution Natural range: eastern Pacific coast of North America from Alaska southward to parts of Mexico; introduced into numerous countries

Status Not threatened

Barbeled Dragonfish

The 9.5-inch (24-cm) stoplight loosejaw (*Malacosteus niger*) occurs at depths down to 8,200 feet (2,500 m) in the Atlantic (from Greenland to Scotland), Indian (from the Gulf of Aden to the Bay of Bengal), and Pacific Oceans (China, Australia, and New Zealand east to South America and north to British Columbia).

Common name Barbeled dragonfish

Family Stomiidae

Subfamilies Astronesthinae (snaggletooths), Stomiinae (scaly dragonfish), Chauliodontinae (viperfish), Melanostomiinae (scaleless black dragonfish), Idiacanthinae (black dragonfish), Malacosteinae (loosejaws)

Order Stomiiformes

Number of species Around 278 in some 27 genera

Size From about 1 in (2.5 cm) to about 20 in (50 cm)

Key features Elongated to very elongated body; body naked except in 2 species that may have scales or scalelike markings plus a jellylike covering; chin barbel present in most species; mouth typically large; numerous fanglike teeth, very long in many species; adipose fin absent in most subfamilies; snaggletooths and viperfish have an additional adipose fin in front of anal fin; all species have photophores, usually in large numbers, mainly along lower half of body and belly; also photophores at tip of chin barbel and on cheeks in many species; majority are dark-colored, many are black

Breeding Breeding and mating behavior unknown; eggs and larvae planktonic; larvae often quite different than adult; most extreme differences found in black dragonfish, whose males and females are also different

Diet Crustaceans and fish; large prey taken even by modest-sized individuals

Habitat Daily migrations made by many species, rising to shallower depths during night; adults of some species occur at or near surface during hours of darkness, descending to depths in excess of 9,850 ft (3,000 m)

Distribution Atlantic, Indian, and Pacific Oceans

Status Not threatened

Marine Hatchetfish

The 3.3-inch (8.4-cm) Pacific hatchetfish (*Argyropelecus affinis*) occurs in the Atlantic from the Gulf of Mexico east to the Gulf of Guinea, as well as the Indian and Pacific Oceans. It is mainly found between 985 and 2,130 feet (300–650 m), but it can go as deep as 12,700 feet (3,870 m).

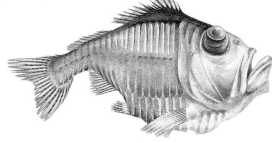

Common name Marine hatchetfish (pearlsides, constellationfish, and allies)

Family Sternoptychidae

Subfamilies Maurolicinae (pearlsides and constellationfish); Sternoptychinae (marine hatchetfish)

Order Stomiiformes

Number of species About 71 in 10 genera

Size From around 0.8 in (2 cm) to 5.5 in (14 cm)

Key features Maurolicinae: elongated body, never compressed; mouth directed at upward angle; eyes almost central on head in normal direction or above center and directed upward; Sternoptychinae: deep, extremely compressed body; mouth directed nearly vertically; eyes in top half of head, directed upward, telescopic in some species; keel-like chest; bladelike structure formed from pterygiophores in front of dorsal fin; rear of body slim (the hatchet "handle"); all speces have photophores (light-producing organs), some inside mouth

Breeding Unknown for most species, but eggs and larvae planktonic; pearlsides (*Maurolicus* spp.) mature in 1 year, spawn March to September, producing 200–500 eggs; constellationfish (*Valenciennellus tripunctulatus*) may only live for 1 year but spawn many times, producing 100–360 eggs each time

Diet Predominantly invertebrates, including copepods; some species also eat small fish

Habitat Most are deepwater species though not living on the bottom; depth ranges from the surface down to more than 12,000 ft (3,660 m); many hatchetfish never rise above 650 ft (200 m), some remain in deeper water at 1,300 ft (400 m)

Distribution Atlantic, Indian, and Pacific Oceans

Status Not threatened

Telescopefish

The 8.7-inch (22-cm) gigantura (*Gigantura chuni*) lives deep in tropical waters of the Atlantic, Indian, and Pacific Oceans. As the larvae develop, they lose their adipose and pelvic fins along with numerous skull bones and the swim bladder.

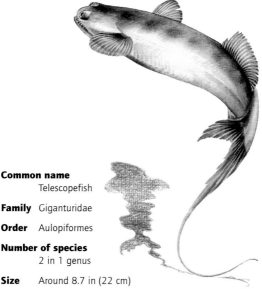

Common name
Telescopefish

Family Giganturidae

Order Aulopiformes

Number of species
2 in 1 genus

Size Around 8.7 in (22 cm)

Key features Elongated, scaleless body covered in loose skin; head blunt; large mouth armed with many sharp teeth that can be lowered; large tubular eyes near top of head; pelvic and adipose fins present in juveniles, absent in adults; pectoral fins directly behind and above gill covers; dorsal and anal fins set back, especially anal; caudal fin strongly forked with extended rays in lower lobe; elastic and extendable stomach; silvery color

Breeding Unknown; larvae very different from adults, with a duck-billed head, small mouth, eyes in normal position (not on stalks), body deepest in the middle, tapering at both ends, full complement of fins including adipose and pelvic fins

Diet Predominantly fish

Habitat Deep, cold marine waters; not found on bottom

Distribution *Gigantura chuni* mainly in tropical regions of Atlantic, Indian, and Pacific Oceans; *G. indica* in tropical and subtropical latitudes of all oceans

Status Not threatened, but although *G. indica* has a wide distribution, it is reported to be rare

Lizardfish

The 12.5-inch (32-cm) gracile lizardfish (*Saurida gracilis*) occurs in shallow lagoons and coral reefs in the Indo-Pacific from the Red Sea and East Africa to the Great Barrier Reef north to Hawaii and Japan. This active predator feeds on fish at night.

Common name Lizardfish

Family Synodontidae

Subfamilies Synodontinae (lizardfish), Harpadontinae (Bombay duck), Bathysaurinae

Order Aulopiformes

Number of species About 64 in 5 genera

Size From 3.5 in (9 cm) to around 30 in (78 m)

Key features Elongated body with large, toothed mouth in all species; eyes large in all, but Bombay ducks have very small eyes; all fins well formed, adipose fin may be absent in Bathysaurinae and some lizardfish; scales over whole body but confined to lateral line and posterior half of body in Bombay ducks; lateral line scales enlarged in Bathysaurinae; variable colors, often mottled

Breeding Eggs and sperm are scattered, then abandoned; sexes separate in all but two species, which are synchronous hermaphrodites (both male and female at same time)— deep-sea lizardfish (*Bathysaurus ferox*) and highfin lizardfish (*B. mollis*)

Diet Fish and invertebrates, primarily crustaceans

Habitat Relatively shallow water like coral reefs and rocky or sandy bottoms; Bathysaurinae occur in deeper, colder waters at depths of 15,750 ft (4,800 m) for 1 species; Bombay ducks enter estuaries, swimming upriver in prebreeding migrations; Synodontinae spend much of their time sitting on the bottom or buried in the substratum with just their eyes showing

Distribution Atlantic, Indian, and Pacific Oceans

Status Not threatened

Barracudinas and Daggertooths

The 15-inch (38-cm) Antarctic jonasfish (*Notolepis coatsi*) is probably circumglobal in Antarctic waters and is found from the surface down to 6,560 feet (2,000 m). It feeds exclusively on krill. It belongs to the family Paralepididae (barracudinas).

Common name
Barracudinas and daggertooths

Families Paralepididae (barracudinas), Anotopteridae (daggertooths)

Order Aulopiformes

Number of species Paralepididae: around 54 in 12 genera; Anotopteridae: 3 in 1 genus

Size From 2.2 in (5.5 cm) to 4.8 ft (1.5 m)

Key features Elongated bodies, more so in daggertooths; pointed, well-toothed mouths; dorsal and adipose fins in barracudinas; dorsal absent in daggertooths, but adipose fin well developed and set well back close to forked tail; anal fin has 20–50 rays in barracudinas, 14–16 in daggertooths; pelvic fins tiny in daggertooths; body scales present or absent in barracudinas, absent in daggertooths; silvery along sides and belly, darker along back

Breeding Eggs and sperm are scattered, then abandoned; some species are hermaphroditic; one daggertooth—the South Ocean daggertooth (*Anotopterus vorax*)—stops feeding before breeding, loses its teeth, and dies after spawning; eggs and larvae are planktonic in all species

Diet Predominantly fish; also crustaceans, squid, worms, and other invertebrates

Habitat Midwater zones from around 100 ft (30 m) or surface in some species down to between 9,020 ft (2,750 m) and 10,800 ft (3,290 m) in others

Distribution Barracudinas found in all oceans, including Arctic and Antarctic; daggertooths in Antarctic, Atlantic, and Pacific Oceans

Status Not threatened

Lancetfish

The 6.5-foot (2-m) longnose lancetfish (*Alepisaurus ferox*) is found in both the Pacific, from Japan and Alaska south to Chile and Australia, and the Atlantic, from Maine and Iceland south to the Mediterranean and South Africa. With its large, fanged mouth it preys on cephalopods, crustaceans, and other fish.

Common name Lancetfish

Family Alepisauridae

Order Aulopiformes

Number of species 2 in 1 genus

Size Up to 6.5 ft (2 m)

Key features Slim, elongated body covered with pores but no scales; head pointed, particularly in longnose lancetfish (*Alepisaurus ferox*); large eyes; jaws have strong, pointed teeth with 2 large, fanglike teeth on palate; sail-like dorsal fin with up to 48 rays but no spines, originating above gill covers and extending along most of the back; dorsal fin can be lowered into a groove; adipose fin present; caudal fin strongly forked; pale along sides and iridescent (shiny), darker along the back; fins dark or black; row of white spots in shortnose lancetfish (*A. brevirostris*)

Breeding Behavior unknown; both species are hermaphroditic; eggs and larvae planktonic

Diet Predominantly fish; also invertebrates such as cephalopods including squid and octopuses

Habitat Open oceanic waters from surface down to 6,000 ft (1,830 m)

Distribution Longnose lancetfish: Pacific and Atlantic Oceans extending into Mediterranean Sea down to South Africa and northward to Iceland; shortnose lancetfish: all major oceans

Status Not threatened

Lanternfish

The 3-inch (7.9-cm) metallic lanternfish (*Myctophum affine*) occurs in the Atlantic from Canada to Angola at depths between 985 and 1,970 feet (300–600 m). It feeds on plankton.

Common name Lanternfish

Family Myctophidae

Order Myctophiformes

Number of species About 245 in 30 genera

Size From around 0.9 in (2.3 cm) to 12 in (30 cm)

Key features Elongated body, often tapering toward tail; large, blunt head; large mouth, usually extending well beyond large eyes; numerous small, fine, closely set teeth; often large scales: cycloid, or roundish, in most species, ctenoid, or toothed, in a few; all fins well formed; back edge of dorsal fin roughly in line with front edge of anal fin; adipose fin present, supported by a cartilage plate below; forked tail; head and body have numerous photophores, each one overlaid by a modified scale acting as a lens; shallower-living species usually iridescent blue-green above with silvery sides and belly; deeper-living species grayish or brown rather than iridescent

Breeding Sexes told apart by pattern and presence of large photophores near caudal peduncle; breeding behavior unknown; eggs and larvae found among plankton; larvae of some species have short eye stalks, may lack photophores; eye stalks absorbed, photophores develop during early stages; spawning restricted to several months (March to August) or all year round in Diogenes lanternfish (*Diogenichthys laternatus*); eggs fertilized externally in most species but internally in at least Diogenes lanternfish

Diet Small invertebrates like euphasiids (luminescent, shrimplike crustaceans)

Habitat Open ocean often far from land; many species occur near the surface at night, migrating during day to deep water around 3,940 ft (1,200 m)

Distribution Global from Arctic to Antarctic Oceans

Status Not threatened

Crestfish

The 6.5-foot (2-m) crested oarfish (*Lophotus lacepede*) occurs in warmer waters of both the Atlantic and the Pacific, feeding on anchovies and squid.

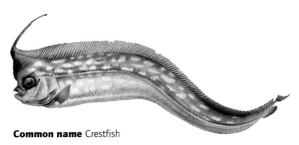

Common name Crestfish

Family Lophotidae

Order Lampridiformes

Number of species 3 in 2 genera

Size From around 4.9 ft (1.5 m) to 6.5 ft (2 m)

Key features Extremely elongated, ribbonlike body; head blunt but with projecting forehead extended into a long, horizontal, hornlike structure in the unicorn crestfish (*Eumecichthys fiski*); mouth extremely extendable; eyes large; dorsal fin originates at tip of forehead and extends to tail; caudal fin small; anal fin very small, positioned close to tail; pelvic fins usually absent; adipose fin absent; small pectoral fins located close to gill covers; scales absent or small and easily dislodged, giving scaleless appearance; silvery base with dark vertical bands in unicorn crestfish, speckling in other 2 species; fins red in all 3 species; when alarmed or needing to make a quick escape, can produce black or dark-brown inklike substance from special organ close to the gut

Breeding Behavior unknown; eggs and larvae are planktonic; eggs of crested oarfish (*Lophotus lacepede*) covered in amber-colored spines

Diet Mainly fish, squid, and other invertebrates

Habitat Open-water species sometimes found close to surface or at depths exceeding 3,300 ft (1,000 m)

Distribution Found in most oceans

Status Not threatened

Ribbonfish

The 9.8-foot (3-m) peregrine ribbonfish (*Trachipterus trachypterus*) occurs at depths down to 1,640 feet (500 m) in the eastern Atlantic from the Mediterranean to South Africa and in the Pacific from Japan south to New Zealand and Chile. It swims with its head up and feeds on squid and midwater fish.

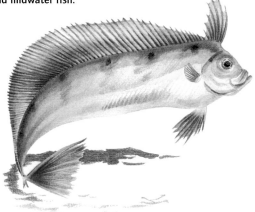

Common name Ribbonfish (dealfish)

Family Trachipteridae

Order Lampridiformes

Number of species 10 in 3 genera (*Desmodema, Trachipterus, Zu*)

Size From 3.6 ft (1.1 m) to 9.8 ft (3 m)

Key features Elongated body tapers to varying degrees; head usually large; snout either steeply sloping or pointed; large mouth and eyes; dorsal fin extends from head to tail, first few rays generally extended; tail large or small, either with just the upper lobe present or (additionally) with much-reduced lower lobe rays; tail at sharp angle to body, often perpendicular; anal and adipose fins absent; pelvic fins have very few rays (even just 1) or absent; pectoral fins directly behind gill covers; body naked (scales are easily dislodged); usually silvery, sometimes speckled; some species: distinctive spots along back

Breeding Behavior unknown; eggs and larvae planktonic; egg surface frequently with irregularities such as tiny "pits"; larvae look very different than adults, with numerous filamentlike growths that gradually disappear

Diet Fish and squid; also crustaceans

Habitat Open ocean at depths ranging from the surface down to 3,300 ft (1,000 m); some species enter brackish water or found close to shore

Distribution Arctic, Atlantic (into the Mediterranean), Indian, and Pacific Oceans

Status Not threatened

Oarfish

The 36-foot (11-m) oarfish, or king-of-the-herrings (*Regalecus glesne*), occurs in the Atlantic (including the Mediterranean), Indo-Pacific, and Pacific Oceans from southern California to Chile. It lives at great depths between 66 and 3,300 feet (20–1,000 m) and feeds on crustaceans, small fish, and squid.

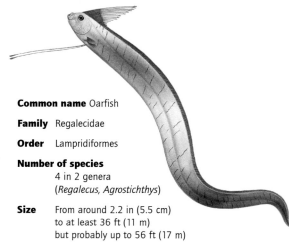

Common name Oarfish

Family Regalecidae

Order Lampridiformes

Number of species
    4 in 2 genera
    (*Regalecus, Agrostichthys*)

Size From around 2.2 in (5.5 cm)
    to at least 36 ft (11 m)
    but probably up to 56 ft (17 m)

Key features Elongated, ribbonlike body; blunt head; large extendable mouth; teeth absent; eyes relatively small; dorsal fin with extremely long base originating above eye and extending to tail; front rays extended ending in small flaps; tail also has extended rays; anal and adipose fins absent; pelvic fins extended with long, paddlelike structures and flap at tips; pectoral fins small and located close to gill covers; body scaleless; silvery blue with dark blotches and streaks; reddish fins

Breeding Behavior unknown; spawning occurs during second half of year; larvae bearing extremely long rays on front of dorsal fin have been collected near surface

Diet Mostly free-swimming, small invertebrates, particularly euphasiids (luminescent, shrimplike crustaceans); also squid and small fish

Habitat Open ocean down to at least 3,300 ft (1,000 m); can also occur at relatively shallow depths but in open water; specimens occasionally washed up on beaches

Distribution All oceans, extending into the Mediterranean Sea for 1 species

Status Not threatened

Beardfish

The 19-inch (48-cm) stout beardfish (*Polymixia nobilis*) occurs in the Atlantic Ocean around the Azores, Madeira, and Canary Islands west to the Caribbean and down to the top of South America. It has a depth range of between 330 and 2,530 feet (100–770 m), and is found on semihard and soft bottoms of the continental shelf and slope.

Common name Beardfish (barbudofish)

Family Polymixiidae

Order Polymixiiformes

Number of species Probably 10 in 1 genus

Size From around 5.7 in (14.5 cm) to about 19 in (48 cm)

Key features Moderately elongated body, mostly long, oval-shaped and compressed; blunt snout, large mouth; two prominent chin barbels, or "beard"; jaws with fine teeth; eyes large; all fins well formed; adipose fin absent; caudal fin strongly forked; dorsal and anal fins have spines at the front (4–6 and 4, respectively); pelvic fin has spinelike ray at front; scales on body and most of head; generally silvery with darker colors along back; fins may be darker throughout or carry distinct dark spots, blotches, or tips

Breeding Unknown

Diet Bottom-dwelling invertebrates, including crustaceans; also squid, cuttlefish, and fish

Habitat Usually deep water below 820 ft (250 m); some in shallow water at around 60 ft (18 m); stout beardfish (*Polymixia nobilis*) extend to 2,530 ft (770 m); most occur close to semihard, sandy, or muddy bottoms

Distribution Tropical and subtropical regions of Atlantic, Indian, and Pacific Oceans; some species (*P. yuni* and *P. salagomeziensis*) have extremely restricted ranges, only found at 1 location or in 1 small area

Status Not threatened

Trout-perch

The blunt-nosed trout-perch (*Percopsis omiscomaycus*) is found in lakes and the deep-flowing pools of creeks and rivers in Canada and the U.S. It grows to 8 inches (20 cm) in length.

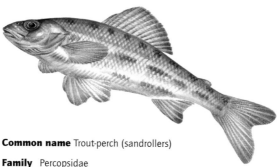

Common name Trout-perch (sandrollers)

Family Percopsidae

Order Percopsiformes

Number of species 2 in 1 genus, *Percopsis*

Size Up to 8 in (20 cm) long, although Columbia trout-perch (*P. transmontana*) usually less than half this size

Key features Small, silvery fish with delicate fins; first rays of dorsal and anal fins form spines; fleshy adipose fin; body, but not head, covered in rough ctenoid scales

Breeding Spawns several times in late spring and summer; usually only lives long enough to breed for 2 or 3 years; spawning occurs in shallow areas—over sandbars or in small, gravelly tributary streams; female ripe with eggs usually attended by several males, who induce her to spawn by pressing themselves close to her sides; fertilized eggs sink to the bottom and stick to gravel or sand; no parental care; hatching takes about 1 week

Diet Carnivorous; mainly small aquatic invertebrates, including crustaceans, mollusks, and insect larvae

Habitat Fresh water

Distribution Widespread throughout most of Canada and northern U.S., including Alaska

Status Secure overall, although many local populations are vulnerable to extinction

Cavefish

Like other cave-dwelling species in the family, the 4.5-inch (11-cm) northern cavefish (*Amblyopsis spelaea*) eats little, breeds slowly, and moves no more than is necessary. Cavefish are difficult to spook—even if they come unexpectedly into contact with another living thing, they turn calmly to one side and move unhurriedly on their way.

Common name Cavefish (swampfish)

Family Amblyopsidae

Order Percopsiformes

Number of species 6 in 4 genera

Size Up to 5 in (13 cm) long

Key features Pale, spindle-shaped fish; single dorsal and anal fins of similar size, each with 7–12 rays located well back on body; in *Typhlichthys subterraneus* first 1 or 2 rays are spiny; in all other species rays are soft and usually branched near tips; large, soft-rayed, rounded tail fin; most species have only 1 set of paired fins, the pectorals, which are roughly oval; pelvic fins absent in all but northern cavefish (*Amblyopsis spelaea*), in which they are present but very small with 3–5 soft rays; vestigial, nonfunctional eyes in cave-dwelling species; 4 species live exclusively in caves and are typically slow moving

Breeding Little is known, but cave species appear to brood eggs and larvae in gill chambers

Diet Small invertebrates such as insects, spiders, myriapods, and other crustaceans

Habitat Caves, springs, and swamps

Distribution Restricted to limestone regions of southeastern U.S., particularly the Mississippi basin

Status IUCN lists Ozark cavefish (*A. rosae*), the northern cavefish, and *Typhlichthys subterraneus* as Vulnerable; and Alabama cavefish (*Speoplatyrhinus poulsoni*) as Critically Endangered

Pirate Perch

Common name Pirate perch

Scientific name *Aphredoderus sayanus*

Family Aphredoderidae

Order Percopsiformes

Size Up to 5 in (13 cm) in length

Key features Small, scaly fish with 1 large dorsal fin, square tail fin, and single anal fin; first 3 rays of dorsal and first 2–3 rays of anal fins modified into spines; distinctive positioning of anus (or vent): as fish grows and matures, anus migrates from usual position toward the back end of body until it is located just beneath the gill openings on the throat in a fully mature adult

Breeding Spawns in early spring; mature eggs attached to vegetation or pond debris

Diet Carnivorous; mainly insect larvae, crustaceans, and smaller fish

Habitat Freshwater ponds, lakes, and slow-flowing rivers

Distribution Eastern U.S. from New York to Texas and inland throughout the Mississippi basin to the Great Lakes

Status Not threatened, but recent surveys suggest species may be in decline

Pearlfish

The pearlfish (*Echiodon drummondi*) grows to a length of up to 12 inches (30 cm). To protect itself from predators, the pearlfish will enter the vent (anus) of a sea cucumber.

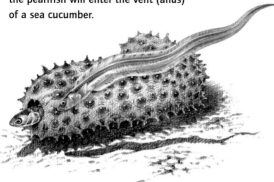

Common name Pearlfish (cucumber fish)

Family Carapidae

Order Ophidiiformes

Number of species 32 in 7 genera

Size Up to 12 in (30 cm) long, usually smaller

Key features Long, very narrow body often tapering to a point at tail end; little thicker than a knifeblade; body fringed with short, continuous fin; no tail fin; most lack pelvic fins; *Encheliophis* species lack pectoral fins; anus located close to throat; most species commensal or parasitic within the body of an invertebrate host; a few species are free living and predatory

Breeding Pelagic eggs; larvae have long, flexible dorsal spine (vexillum); some species pair for life inside host

Diet Carnivorous; some are parasitic, others use host as lair from which they catch food; free-living species are predatory

Habitat Marine; most species live in shallow tropical and subtropical seas less than 600 feet (200 m) deep; some are temperate

Distribution Worldwide, mostly in warmer waters of tropics and subtropics

Status Not threatened

Cusk Eels

The abyssal brotula (*Abyssobrotula galatheae*) only grows to a length of about 6.5 inches (16.5 cm), but it is the deepest living fish on record.

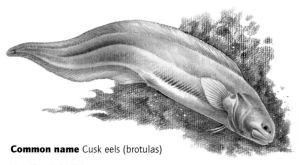

Common name Cusk eels (brotulas)

Family Ophidiidae

Order Ophidiiformes

Number of species Over 200 in about 50 genera

Size From a few inches to 6 feet (1.8 m) long

Key features Mostly medium- to large-sized fish with elongated bodies and long-based dorsal and anal fins; single median fin composed of fused dorsal, anal, and caudal fins; when present, paired fins have soft rays, but pelvic fins, especially, greatly reduced—often little more than single or paired filaments located well forward on fish's body at throat; pelvic fins absent in some *Brotula* species; when approached or disturbed, most cusk eels assume vertical position and start to burrow tailfirst into sediment; can also produce bursts of sound by vibration of the swim bladder—often as a prelude to spawning

Breeding Mostly egg-laying species, although members of related families are livebearers; during breeding season males begin croaking before emerging from burrows at dusk; females produce batches of eggs covered in jelly that swells on contact with water and rises to surface; egg mass breaks up after 24 hours, and eggs hatch on second day

Diet Mostly benthic invertebrates

Habitat Mostly marine; benthic at a variety of depths from littoral zones to ocean trenches, but greatest diversity occurs in tropical and subtropical waters; some freshwater cave-dwellers

Distribution In all the world's oceans

Status Not threatened

Grenadiers

The rough-head grenadier (*Macroumis berglax*) can grow to 3 feet (1 m) in length and is found at depths of 650 feet (200 m) into the abyssal zone.

Common name Grenadiers (rattails, whiptails)

Family Macrouridae

Order Gadiformes

Number of species About 300 species in 38 genera

Size From 4 to 60 in (10–150 cm) long

Key features Highly distinctive, with disproportionately large head and large eyes; head usually blunt but can have short, pointed snout; short body; long, tapering tail fringed with long-based second dorsal and anal fins; anal fin longer than dorsal fin; tail fin absent; most have single chin barbel; in most the upper jaw projects beyond the lower jaw, so the mouth opens downward; some species have light-producing organ on the belly in front of the anus; consists of a small pouch off the gut and contains a colony of symbiotic bacteria harvested from the fish's diet; males have specialized drumming muscles used to strum or vibrate swim blader to attract mates

Breeding Large numbers of tiny eggs released and fertilized externally during mass spawning events; no parental care occurs

Diet Carnivorous; most species are indiscriminate predators and will eat anything of suitable size that comes their way

Habitat Pelagic or lives close to bottom in deep sea

Distribution Worldwide

Status Not threatened

Hake

The merluccid luminous hake (*Steindachneria argentea*) grows to a maximum length of 12 inches (30 cm). It ranges in the Atlantic from around Florida south through the Gulf of Mexico to Venezuela and lives at depths of between 1,310 and 1,640 feet (400–500 m).

Common name Hake

Families Merlucciidae (true hake), Steindachneriidae (luminous hake), Macruronidae (southern hake), Phycidae (phycine hake, rockling)

Order Gadiformes

Number of species 13 species of true hake, plus 36 species in three related families

Size Up to 4 ft (1.2 m) long

Key features Elongated, streamlined fish with a tapering body; 2 or 3 dorsal fins sometimes merging with tail and anal fin; body usually countershaded in blue and silver and covered in medium to large cycloid scales; barbels present on face in some species, and all have large mouth and sharp teeth

Breeding Spawn spring and summer or all year round; no parental care; eggs small and drift in midwater for 2–3 days before hatching into larvae about 0.1 in (2.5 mm) long; young grow fast

Diet Carnivorous, highly cannibalistic (in some hakes up to 50 percent of diet consists of members of their own species); will eat anything they can swallow, starting with small crustaceans such as copepods and krill, moving on to small squid and other fish as they grow; ambush feeders, using large eyes to locate prey before grabbing it with distinctive "snap-and-bite" style of attack

Habitat Marine, moderate to deep water; rest on seafloor by day; hunt in midwater; nocturnal, solitary; migrate annually and daily

Distribution Atlantic, Southern, and Pacific Oceans

Status Not threatened

Cod and Haddock

The Atlantic cod (*Gadus morhua*) can grow to 50 inches (1.3 m). This popular food fish occurs in the North Atlantic from Cape Hatteras to Ungava Bay around Greenland and Iceland east to the Barents Sea and south to the Bay of Biscay. As omnivorous predators, they eat all kinds of marine invertebrates and fish, even young cod.

Common name Cod and haddock

Family Gadidae

Order Gadiformes

Number of species About 30 in 15 genera

Size From 6 to 50 inches (15–130 cm)

Key features Slim, torpedo-shaped body; three dorsal fins; two anal fins; paired pelvic fins in front of pectorals; most species with conspicuous barbel on chin

Breeding Spawn in spring; reach adulthood at 2 to 4 years

Diet Aquatic invertebrates and other fish; sometimes smaller individuals of same or related species; strong, needlelike teeth ideal for grasping slippery, wriggling prey; in species that have chin barbel, it is covered with "tastebuds" and can be used to sample potential food before ingestion

Habitat Demersal and benthopelagic (living close to, but not on, bottom) in marine, brackish, and fresh waters; gregarious, often migratory

Distribution Predominantly a Northern Hemisphere family, in Arctic, Atlantic, and Pacific Oceans and adjoining rivers and seas; greatest numbers congregate where the warm waters of the Gulf Stream collide with cool Arctic currents, creating highly productive zone where their preferred foods are abundant

Status IUCN lists Atlantic cod (*Gadus morhua*) and haddock (*Melanogrammus aeglefinus*) as Vulnerable; of other species some are stable, some Critically Endangered

Deep-Sea Cod

The female of the tadpole codling (*Salilota australis*) is bigger than the male and can grow as long as 20 inches (50 cm). It inhabits depths between 100 and 3,300 feet (30–1,000 m) in the southwest Pacific and southwest Atlantic.

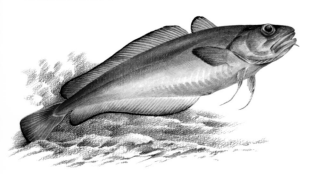

Common name Deep-sea cod

Families Moridae (moras and codlings), Rancipitidae (tadpole fish), Euclichthyidae (eucla cod), Muranolepididae (eel cod), Bregmacerotidae (codlets), Melanonidae (pelagic cod)

Order Gadiformes

Number of species About 120 in total, mostly in Moridae

Size Varied from just a few inches to 2 ft (60 cm)

Key features Varied appearance; most species have long body, tapering tail, and elongated dorsal and anal fins; benthic, pelagic, and surface-dwelling species; some have luminous structures

Breeding Little known

Diet Carnivorous; marine invertebrates and smaller fish caught close to seabed or in midwater

Habitat Marine

Distribution Mostly Southern Hemisphere; all but Bregmacerotidae are fish of temperate and cold waters

Status Most species thought to be not threatened, but many are not well known enough to say for sure

Toadfish

The 15-inch (38-cm) American oyster toadfish (*Opsanus tau*) is also known as the oyster cracker. This venomous species occurs in the western Atlantic from Massachusetts to the West Indies. Living up to its name, this fish eats oysters, other shellfish, most invertebrates, and smaller fish. It is confined to shallow water.

Common name Toadfish (midshipmen, venomous toadfish)

Family Batrachoididae

Subfamily Batrachoidinae (toadfish), Porichthyinae (midshipmen), Thalassophryninae (venomous toadfish)

Order Batrachoidiformes

Number of species About 69 species in 19 genera

Size Up to 15 in (38 cm) long

Key features Large head; very wide mouth; ribs reduced; pelvic fins jugular with one spine and 2–3 soft rays; nocturnal; usually solitary; highly vocal; venomous toadfish have hollow dorsal spines that can deliver poison into the flesh of a victim, causing tissue damage and severe pain

Breeding In shallow water in spring and summer; males use vocalizations or bioluminescence to attract a mate; males prepare nest in cavity, usually a rock but sometimes in discarded can or other garbage; eggs are large; some species show parental care

Diet Omnivorous but mainly other fish, mollusks, and crustaceans

Habitat Marine; bottom-dwelling; toadfish in shallow water, midshipmen in deeper areas of continental shelf

Distribution Widespread in tropical and temperate seas, but most species restricted to Atlantic and Pacific waters off North and South America

Status IUCN lists 6 species as Vulnerable

Goosefish

The American goosefish (*Lophius americanus*) can reach lengths of over 4 feet (1.2 m). This grim, voracious predator, found at depths of 330 feet (100 m) in the western Atlantic, will eat anything that comes close to its lure, including fish and all kinds of invertebrates.

Common name Goosefish

Family Lophiidae

Order Lophiiformes

Number of species 25 species in 4 genera

Size Up to 4 ft (1.2 m) long

Key features Huge, broad head tapers to dorsoventrally flattened body; enormous mouth lined with many hundreds of teeth; lower jaw fringed with small frills of skin; first dorsal fin modified into mobile fishing lure that can be waved in imitation of a scrap of food while its owner remains invisible, often partially buried; solitary; nocturnal

Breeding Spawning takes place in spring in deep water, when up to 2.5 million eggs are released in a mass of floating jelly; young goosefish have very long ventral fins that gradually shrink as they develop; larvae spend early lives feeding on plankton near the surface and head for seafloor when they reach about 3 in (8 cm) long

Diet Carnivorous; mainly other fish attracted by lure and swallowed whole, but also small sharks, large crabs, and even diving seabirds

Habitat Marine; benthic (bottom-dwelling)

Distribution More or less cosmopolitan; in all major oceans and adjoining seas

Status Not threatened

Frogfish

As its name suggests, the 4.5-inch (11-cm) longlure frogfish (*Antennarius multiocellatus*), also known as the flagpole frogfish, has a long dorsal spine modified into a lure for attracting prey. This species occurs down to 200 feet (60 m) in the Atlantic from Bermuda and the Bahamas south to Brazil and east to the Ascension Islands and the Azores. It eats small fish and crustaceans lured close enough to ambush.

Common name Frogfish

Family Antennariidae

Order Lophiiformes

Number of species 43 species in 14 genera

Size From about 1 to 13 in (0.5–33 cm) in length

Key features Body often almost spherical; may be dorsoventrally flattened; paired fins are muscular and armlike; first ray of dorsal fin modified into fishing lure, shape and size of which varies according to species; can change skin color to match surroundings in just a few hours; various strange flaps and frills also help break up the body outline, creating perfect camouflage; solitary; nocturnal

Breeding Fertilized eggs float in gelatinous rafts; young live and feed in plankton community

Diet Carnivorous; catch smaller fish and invertebrates using lure that looks like a small, darting fish when waved around; occasionally cannibalistic

Habitat Marine; most species benthic (bottom-dwelling), although sargassum fish (*Histrio histrio*) live in midwater with dense seaweed growth.

Distribution Widespread in tropical and subtropical oceans and adjoining seas around the world

Status Not threatened

Batfish

The 4-inch (10-cm) pancake batfish (*Halieutichthys aculeatus*) is the sole member of its genus. It moves its flattened, scaleless body over the seafloor using its fleshy pectoral and pelvic fins.

Common name Batfish

Family Ogcocephalidae

Order Lophiiformes

Number of species 62 species in 9 genera

Size Up to 14 in (35 cm) long; usually much less

Key features Greatly flattened, pancakelike or boxlike head; large horizontal mouth; narrow body trunk and tail; body supported on large, armlike pectoral fins; solitary ambush predators, tempting prey within range by means of fleshy lure on the end of retractable spine on the vestigial dorsal fin; prefer "walking" over seabed on modified fins to swimming

Breeding Pelagic larvae similar to those of other anglers

Diet Carnivorous; an ambush predator that takes variety of vertebrate and invertebrate prey, including crustaceans and fish;

Habitat Marine; bottom dwelling

Distribution Widespread in all the tropical oceans and many adjoining seas

Status Not threatened

Deep-Sea Anglerfish

Female humpback anglerfish (*Melanocetus johnsonii*), shown here, grow no larger than 7 inches (18 cm), but they dwarf the males, which rarely exceed 1 inch (2.5 cm) in length. The species lives in deep water in tropical and temperate oceans.

Common name Deep-sea anglerfish

Families Linophrynidae, Caulophrynidae, Neoceratiidae, Melanocetidae, Himantolophidae, Diceratiidae, Oneirodidae, Thaumatichthyidae, Centrophrynidae, Ceratiidae, Gigantactinidae

Order Lophiiformes

Number of species About 174 species in 11 families

Size Most spp. less than 8 in (20 cm) long; largest sea devils up to 40 in (1 m); males always very small

Key features Most with globular body; skin covered in blotches and colored in dull shades of black, brown, or olive-green; head large; mouth often gapes to reveal rows of needle-sharp teeth; lack pelvic fins; fishing lure emanates from fin ray and varies from short stub to elaborate, fleshy growth, usually bioluminescent; solitary

Breeding Dwarf males either free living or parasitic on females; eggs spawned in gelatinous mass; hatch into pelagic larvae

Diet Females carnivorous; prey on other fish and deep-sea invertebrates attracted by fishing lure that contains bioluminescent bacteria to illuminate the tip (known as the esca); free-living males feed on plankton; male parasites share resources via blood connection with female and are unable to survive without her

Habitat Marine; pelagic in deep water

Distribution Tropical and subtropical oceans worldwide

Status Little known because habitat so inaccessible

Mullets

The gray mullet (*Mugil cephalus*) is also known as the flathead mullet. The largest member of the family Mugilidae, it can grow to a length of 4 feet (1.2 m).

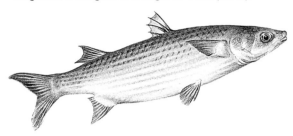

Common name Mullets

Family Mugilidae

Order Mugiliformes

Number of species 75 species in around 17 genera

Size From around 4 in (10 cm) to 4 ft (1.2 m); majority above 8 in (20 cm)

Key features Elongated body; head flattened on top; mouth moderately sized; small teeth or no teeth; fins well formed but no adipose fin; 2 dorsal fins widely separated—first bears 4 spines, second soft rays; pectoral fins close to back edge of gill cover (operculum) high up on body; pelvic fins on front half of belly; anal fin with 3 spines at front; caudal fin forked; blue-green coloration above shading to whitish-silvery along belly; other colors also present

Breeding Spawning summer to fall, or even winter, in seas and estuaries; eggs scattered in open; hatching may only take 1.5 days

Diet Algae, plants, plant debris, tiny free-floating organisms (zooplankton), and organic matter, including small invertebrates sifted from mouthfuls of soft sediments

Habitat Marine, close to coastal waters; many migrate between sea and fresh water, return to brackish or marine environments for spawning

Distribution All tropical, subtropical, and temperate seas

Status Not threatened

Rainbowfish and Allies

The rainbowfish (*Melanotaenia goldiei*) is a member of the family Melanotaeniidae. It occurs in New Guinea, Irian Jaya, and the Aru Islands, where it frequents swampy backwaters, creeks, and rivers. Length to 4.5 inches (11.5 cm).

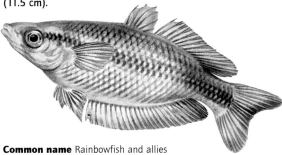

Common name Rainbowfish and allies

Families Bedotiidae (Madagascan rainbowfish), Melanotaeniidae (rainbowfish), Pseudomugilidae (blue-eyes), Telmatherinidae (Celebes rainbowfish)

Order Atheriniformes

Number of species Bedotiidae: around 9 in 2 genera; Melanotaeniidae: around 67 in 6 genera; Psuedomugilidae: around 15 in 3 genera; Telmatherinidae: around 17 in 5 genera

Size Bedotiidae: from 2 in (5 cm) to 5.5 in (14 cm); Melanotaeniidae: from 2 in (5 cm) to 6 in (15 cm); Psuedomugilidae: from 1 in (2.5 cm) to 2.4 in (6 cm); Telmatherinidae: from 1.8 in (4.5 cm) to 8 in (20 cm)

Key features Body elongate from compressed to rounded; head pointed to moderately rounded; large eyes; all species have 2 dorsal fins, first with spines; fins well formed; tail forked; some fins carry filamentlike extensions; coloration extremely variable but often striking; males more intensely colored

Breeding All egg scatterers; eggs take up to 2 weeks to hatch; no parental care

Diet Small invertebrates; most Bedotiidae and Melanotaeniidae feed on plant material

Habitat Fresh water, brackish water, and a few species in the sea (mangrove areas)

Distribution Bedotiidae: Madagascar; Melanotaeniidae: Australia and New Guinea; Pseudomugilidae: Australia, New Guinea, eastern Indonesia; Telmatherinidae: Sulawesi and islands of Misool and Batanta (western New Guinea)

Status IUCN lists 60 species as under various levels of threat

Silversides

The sand smelt (*Atherina presbyter*) is found in the eastern Atlantic Ocean, mainly around the coasts of Britain, southwest Europe, and North Africa. It grows to about 8 inches (20 cm) in length.

Common name Silversides

Family Atherinidae

Order Atheriniformes

Number of species Around 165 in 25 genera

Size From 2.8 in (7.5 cm) to 17.5 in (44.5 cm)

Key features Elongated bodies; head pointed or rounded; large eyes; "forehead" slopes upward; dorsal profile straight; mouth located at tip of snout; fins well formed; 2 dorsal fins, no adipose fin; 1st dorsal fin with flexible spines, softer 2nd dorsal; pectoral fins high on side and close to gill covers; tail forked; coloration various shades—green-blue on back in marine species; all have characteristic silvery sides; freshwater species patterned with spots and lines

Breeding Egg scatterers except grunion (*Leuresthes tenuis*); spawning season March to April/September; tropical species spawn throughout year; a few, e.g., *Atherinopsis* species such as jacksmelt (*A. californiensis*), spawn in winter; eggs scattered over vegetation or substratum; hatching takes several days or longer

Diet Small floating and drifting invertebrates (zooplankton); small fish

Habitat Marine species in shallow seas; freshwater species in streams, rivers, and lakes

Distribution Seas around the globe; some fresh water in North and South America, Australia, and New Guinea

Status IUCN lists 32 species as under various levels of threat

Ricefish and Allies

The Japanese medaka (*Oryzias latipes*) is a shoaling species about 1.5 inches (4 cm) long. It is distributed in China, South Korea, and Japan, and is reported to be established in Java and Malaysia, as well as having been introduced to many other places.

Common name Ricefish and allies

Family Adrianichthyidae

Order Beloniformes

Number of species Around 25 in 4 genera

Size From 0.8 in (2 cm) to 7 in (18 cm)

Key features Elongated, compressed body; head large; well-formed eyes; mouth directed upward; dorsal profile straight or almost straight; dorsal and anal fins set well back along the body; fins usually well formed; coloration: variable—from transluscent in Malabar ricefish (*Horaichthys setnai)* to spotted and grayish with silvery sides in Sarasin's minnow, *Xenopoecilus saranisorum*

Breeding Eggs fertilized internally or externally; female carries batches of fertilized eggs attached to area around genital opening; eggs released among vegetation

Diet Small insects and aquatic invertebrates; larger species take small fish

Habitat Streams, ditches, canals, or ponds, often with dense plant growth, or in brackish water

Distribution India to Japan and on to the Indo-Australian archipelago

Status IUCN lists 10 species as variously threatened, including 3 Endangered and 2 Critically Endangered

Flying Fish, Needlefish, Sauries

The flying fish (*Exocoetus volitans*) is about 12 inches (30 cm) long. It is found in tropical and subtropical regions of all the world's oceans. It is a "two-winged" species, using only the pectoral fins for flight.

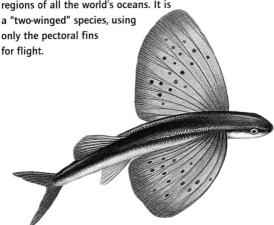

Common name Flying fish, needlefish, and sauries

Families Exocoetidae (flying fish), Belonidae (needlefish), Scomberesocidae (sauries)

Order Beloniformes

Number of species Exocoetidae: 67 in 8 genera; Belonidae: around 45 species in 10 genera; Scomberesocidae: 5 in 3 genera

Size Exocoetidae: from 5.5 in (14 cm) to 20 in (50 cm); Belonidae: from around 1.5 in (4 cm) to 5 ft (1.5 m); Scomberesocidae: from 3 in (7.5 cm) to 20 in (50 cm)

Key features Body elongated; dorsal and anal fins set well back; caudal forked, lobe size varies: in flying fish lower lobe larger than upper with some stiffened rays; in needlefish both lobes similar; in sauries both lobes equal size; pectoral fins large and winglike in flying fish; sauries have series of 5–7 small "fins"; well-formed eyes; flying fish have short jaw; needlefish have beaklike jaws armed with needlelike teeth; sauries may be long beaked or short beaked; coloration: all species deep blue to lighter blue; sides and belly silvery

Breeding Spawning during warmer months in open waters; some needlefish spawn close to coastline; flying fish may spawn among mats of floating seaweeds; all eggs float

Diet Predatory; flying fish feed on plankton; needlefish and sauries feed on smaller fish

Habitat Flying fish and sauries marine; some needlefish marine, but there are 11 freshwater species

Distribution Tropical and temperate regions

Status Not threatened

Halfbeaks

The 2.5–3 inch (6.5–8-cm) long threadjaw halfbeak (*Hemirhamphodon pogonognathus*) is found in fresh and brackish waters in Southeast Asia, where it forms surface shoals that feed on flies and aquatic larvae.

Common name Halfbeaks

Family Hemiramphidae

Order Beloniformes

Number of species 120 in around 13 genera

Size Smaller species from 1.2–1.6 in (3–4 cm); larger marine species up to 13.8 in (35 cm)

Key features Elongated body, with absolutely straight dorsal profile extending from tip of snout to beginning of dorsal fin; stockiest species are Celebes halfbeak (*Nomorhamphus liemi*) and relatives; top jaw much shorter than lower jaw—in the wrestling halfbeak (*Dermogenys pusilla*) lower jaw can be more than twice the length of top jaw; both jaws end in sharp tip; most species have body characteristic of predators hunting just under water surface, i.e., mottled coloration, dorsal and anal fins set well back near caudal fin, and eyes placed high on head; highly aggressive by nature

Breeding Most egg layers, but some produce live young; sperm transfer between male and female takes place via mating organ formed by anal fin modifications (known as an andropodium); internally fertilized eggs take 4–8 weeks to develop; number of young per brood small—as few as 10

Diet Freshwater species hunters of insects and aquatic invertebrates from top layers of water column; many marine species feed on plant material like floating seagrasses

Habitat Most brackish and marine; some found in fresh water

Distribution From Australia to coasts of Americas in tropical and subtropical regions

Status IUCN lists 6 species as under various levels of threat

Rivulines

A native of equatorial Africa, the flamboyant male red lyretail (*Aphyosemion bivittatum*) is one of several species of killifish that have proved popular with aquarists. Length to 2 inches (5 cm).

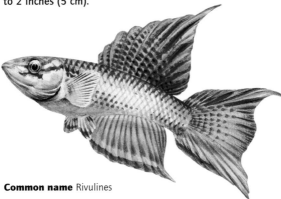

Common name Rivulines

Family Aplocheilidae

Subfamilies Aplocheilinae (Old World rivulines or killifish), Rivulinae (New World rivulines or killifish)

Order Cyprinodontiformes

Number of species Over 275 in 20 genera

Size From around 1.2 in (3 cm) to 2.8 in (7 cm)

Key features Elongated body; some South American *Cynolebias* deeper bodied; snout pointed, as in *Epiplatys* and *Aplocheilus*, or rounded in *Nothobranchius*; eyes large; mouth directed upward; fins well formed; no adipose fin; dorsal and anal fins set well back; tail rounded—extensions in some, e.g., clown killifish (*Epiplatys annulatus*); coloration variable in males—spectacular in many *Aphyosemion* and *Nothobranchius*; females are drabber

Breeding Egg layers; spawning takes place continuously over several weeks; spawning in pairs; eggs laid on plants or buried in bottom mud; hatching from around 2 weeks to several months

Diet Small invertebrates, especially insects

Habitat Streams, ponds, and ditches; many in waters that dry up in summer season

Distribution Aplocheilinae: Africa, Indian subcontinent, Indo-Malayan archipelago; Rivulinae: southern Florida, Cuba into South America as far as Uruguay

Status IUCN lists 17 species as under various levels of threat, including Turner's gaucho (*Campellolebias brucei*) plus 7 *Cynolebias* species from Brazil—Vulnerable; Sakaramy panchax (*Pachypanchax sakaramyi*) from Madagascar—Critically Endangered; Caprivi nothobranch (*Nothobranchius* sp.) from the Caprivi Strip in Namibia—Endangered

Topminnows and Killifish

The mummichog (*Fundulus heteroclitus*) is one of several species that is able to live in a variety of different types of habitats, ranging from the sea to fresh water. Length to 6 inches (15 cm).

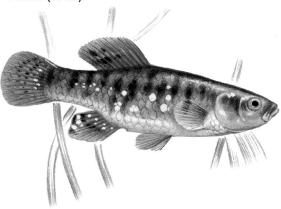

Common name Topminnows and killifish

Family Fundulidae

Order Cyprinodontiformes

Number of species 40 in around 5 genera

Size From 1.4 in (3.5 cm) to 8 in (20 cm); many 3–4 in (7.6–10 cm)

Key features Elongated body; exception is diamond killifish (*Adinia xenica*) with deep body and sharply pointed snout; snout more rounded in most; mouth predominantly directed upward; head flattened; large eyes; dorsal and anal fins set well back; tail fin rounded; coloration variable, often with numerous dark or colored spots on body

Breeding Eggs scattered over a week or longer among vegetation and abandoned; hatching takes several days to over 2 weeks

Diet Small invertebrates including insects

Habitat Freshwater streams and ponds, brackish estuaries and mangrove zones, to coastal stretches and marine lagoons; some, e.g., the mummichog (*Fundulus heteroclitus*) can occupy the whole range

Distribution From Canada southward through North America to the Yucatán (Mexico) and Bermuda and Cuba

Status Not threatened

Pupfish

Aphanius dispar is a nonmigratory, herbivorous species from Sudan. It can tolerate a range of conditions from fresh water to brackish and marine conditions. It lays its eggs among water hyacinths and other vegetation. Length to 2.8 inches (7 cm).

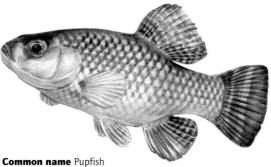

Common name Pupfish

Family Cyprinodontidae

Order Cyprinodontiformes

Number of species Around 100 in 8 genera

Size From around 1 in (2.5 cm) to 8 in (20 cm)

Key features Elongated body, stumpy in some male *Aphanius* and *Cyprinodon*; snout rounded, mouth directed upward; eyes large; all fins, except pelvics, well formed; pelvics very small in some species and absent in Devil's Hole pupfish (*Cyprinodon diabolis*); dorsal fin larger in males than females; tail fin rounded, except in *Orestias*, which has straighter back edge; coloration variable—from almost black to silvery but intense in males; body bands or spots common, particularly in *Aphanius*

Breeding Spawning spring and summer months; eggs scattered among vegetation; some, e.g., Florida flagfish (*Jordanella floridae*), deposited in nest site and guarded by male; hatching takes several days— some up to 10–12 days

Diet Small invertebrates; also plants, especially algae

Habitat Fresh water to brackish and coastal waters, in streams, pools, swamps, lakes, estuaries, and coastal strips

Distribution U. S., Central America, Cuba, Caribbean, northern South America (including Peru); *Aphanius* distributed in North Africa, Spain, Italy, Turkey, Greece, Iran, and Saudi Arabia

Status IUCN lists over 40 species as under various levels of threat

Four-Eyed Fish and Allies

The four-eyed fish *Anableps anableps* is the best-known species in the family. About 12 inches (30 cm) in length, it is found along coasts, estuaries, and in lakes.

Common name Four-eyed fish and allies

Family Anablepidae

Order Cyprinodontiformes

Number of species 13 in 3 genera

Size From around 1 in (2.5 cm) to 13.8 in (35 cm)

Key features Four-eyed fish (*Anableps* spp.) elongate; prominent eyes set high on head; mouth under tip of fleshy snout; dorsal profile straight to the tail; dorsal fin set far back; fins well formed; anal fin in males modified into gonopodium. One-sided livebearers (*Jenynsia* spp.) less elongate; eyes on top half of head; blunt snout; dorsal fin farther forward; gonopodium present. White-eye (*Oxyzgonectes dovii*) elongate; snout pointed; eyes large, positioned centrally on side of head; dorsal profile curved; dorsal fin set well back; fins well formed

Breeding In four-eyed fish and one-sided livebearers eggs fertilized internally; female retains eggs and developing embryos; white-eye is egg layer—eggs fertilized externally and abandoned

Diet Vegetation and small invertebrates

Habitat One-sided livebearers fresh water; four-eyed fish in fresh water and brackish water; white-eye in fresh water and brackish water; all species often in open water

Distribution Four-eyed (*A. anableps*) and largescale four-eyed (*A. microlepis*) in South America: Pacific four-eyed fish (*A. dowii*) in Pacific drainages of Central America; one-sided livebearers South America; white-eye in Panama and Costa Rica

Status Not threatened

Guppies, Swordtails, and Lampeyes

The guppy (*Poecilia reticulata*) is a 2-inch (5-cm) fish originally from parts of South America and the West Indies, but now also introduced into other areas.
This is a female.

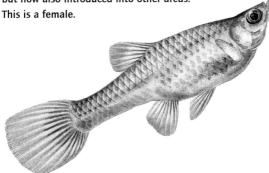

Common name Guppies, swordtails, lampeyes

Family Poeciliidae

Subfamilies Poeciliinae, Fluviphylacinae, Aplocheilichyinae

Order Cyprinodontiformes

Number of species Poeciliinae: around 200 in 20 genera; Fluviphylacinae: 1 species; Aplocheilichyinae: about 100 in around 7 genera

Size From around 0.8 in (2.2 cm) to 8 in (20 cm)

Key features Body shape varies from elongated slim forms with smallish fins to sturdier forms with enlarged fins; upward-directed mouth at tip of snout; eyes large; pectoral fins toward front of belly/chest; in livebearers anal fin is an elongated mating organ; in egg layers anal fin not modified; adipose fin absent; coloration extremely variable

Breeding In livebearers fertilized eggs retained in body until hatching, except in Tommy (*Tomeurus gracilis*); in egg layers eggs scattered among vegetation and abandoned

Diet Invertebrates; some, e.g., piketop livebearer (*Belonesox belizanus*), feed on other fish; also plants, e.g., mollies (some *Poecilia* spp.)

Habitat From shady forest streams to lakes, rivers, estuaries, and coastal waters; most live in surface layers

Distribution Poeciliinae and Fluviphylacinae from Florida to South America; Aplocheilichthyinae in Africa

Status IUCN lists 25 species of livebearer poeciliids as under various levels of threat

Goodeids

The gold sawfin goodeid (*Skiffia francesae*), so called because of its serrated dorsal fin, became extinct in the wild only a decade after its discovery in 1978. It continues to survive in captivity. Length 2 inches (5 cm).

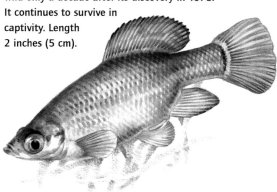

Common name Goodeids (splitfins)

Family Goodeidae

Order Cyprinodontiformes

Number of species Goodeinae: over 35 in 17 genera; Empetrichthyinae: 2 in 2 genera

Size From around 2 in (5 cm) to 8 in (20 cm); most under 4 in (10 cm)

Key features Variable body: elongated and slim, e.g., blue-tailed goodeid (*Goodea toweri*), to stockier, almost hump backed, e.g., male orange- or red-tailed goodeids (*Xenotoca* spp.) and gold sawfin goodeids (*Skiffia francesae*); springfish (*Crenichthys* spp.) more rounded head; fins well formed; egg layers lack pelvic fins; in male livebearers anal fin has a distinct notch—the spermatopodium

Breeding Spans warmer months; in livebearers several broods of large, well-formed young per year; interval between broods 5–8 weeks; egg layers scatter eggs among vegetation; 1 week to hatch

Diet Small invertebrates and plant matter; some predatory

Habitat Goodeines found in slow-flowing or shady water among dense vegetation, mostly in highland areas with cool temperatures (68–75°F/20–24°C); springfish and poolfish (*Empetrichthys* spp.) found in warm-water spring and pool habitats; temperatures for springfish can exceed 90°F (32°C); poolfish in cooler water

Distribution Mesa Central of Mexico (Rio Lerma basin); empetrichthyines restricted to southern Nevada

Status IUCN lists 13 species as under various levels of threat, including 2 species Extinct in the wild but surviving in captivity

Pricklefish and Allies

The 5-inch (13-cm) pricklefish (*Acanthochaenus luetkenii*) lives at depths from 5,430 to 17,415 feet (1,655–5,308 m). It has an immense range from the northwest Atlantic into the Indian and Pacific Oceans.

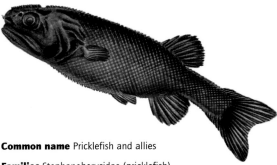

Common name Pricklefish and allies

Families Stephanoberycidae (pricklefish), Melamphaidae (bigscales or ridgeheads), Cetomimidae (flabby whalefish), Barbourisiidae (red or velvet whalefish), Rondeletiidae (redmouth or orangemouth whalefish)

Order Stephanoberyciformes

Number of species Stephanoberycidae: 3 in 3 genera; Melamphaidae: about 38 in 5 genera; Cetomimidae, Barbourisiidae, Rondeletiidae: 23 in about 11 genera

Size From around 0.8–1 in (2.1–2.5 cm) to about 15.8 in (40 cm)

Key features All elongated; head blunt (pricklefish and bigscales), longer-snouted (whalefish); mouth large to very large; eyes very small (flabby whalefish), larger in others; body covered in prickly scales (pricklefish), large scales (bigscales); skin: spiny (red or velvet whalefish), scaleless or smooth in others, or very loose (flabby whalefish: has very pronounced lateral line); dorsal and anal fins sit well back (whalefish), farther forward in all others; pelvic fins absent (flabby whalefish); coloration: often brown to black; red, or velvet, whalefish is bright red

Breeding Few details available; bigscales reportedly scatter eggs and sperm; eggs and larvae are planktonic

Diet Mainly invertebrates and other fish

Habitat Mostly deepwater marine fish; may extend into shallow water during larval stages or within a 24-hour period; all strictly marine, some occurring at great depths

Distribution Worldwide but mainly in Atlantic, Indian, and Pacific Oceans

Status Not threatened

Fangtooths and Allies

The 6-inch (15-cm) common fangtooth (*Anoplogaster cornuta*) occurs between 1,640 and 16,400 feet (500–5,000 m). These predators are, in turn, hunted by tuna and marlin.

Common name Fangtooths and allies

Families Anoplogastridae (fangtooths), Anomalopidae (flashlight or lanterneye fish), Monocentridae (pineapple and pinecone fish), Trachichthyidae (roughies, sawbellies, and slimeheads), Holocentridae (squirrelfish and soldierfish)

Order Beryciformes

Number of species Anoplogastridae: 2 in 1 genus; Anomalopidae: 8 in 6 genera; Monocentridae: 4 in 2 genera; Trachichthyidae: around 44 in 8 genera; Holocentridae: around 83 in 8 genera

Size From 2 in (5 cm) to 30 in (75 cm)

Key features Longish to oval body shape; body scales range from very small to large and platelike; head from blunt to more pointed, moderately large to very large; light organ under eye or on lower jaw; eyes relatively large to large in most species (small in fangtooths); powerful fanglike teeth (fangtooths); 1 dorsal fin (spines in front, soft rays in back); pronounced dorsal fin notch (lanternfish) or 2 separate fins (pineapple fish); variable coloration: yellow through red to brown and black; some species have light or dark patterns, luminescence produced inside bodies

Breeding Few details available; eggs and sperm released into water where fertilization takes place; no parental care; eggs take a few weeks to hatch; larvae usually live among plankton for some time

Diet Mainly fish; some invertebrates

Habitat Relatively shallow tropical and subtropical, also temperate, waters; deepwater species (fangtooth) down to 16,400 ft (5,000 m); many in caves or under ledges during day, rise to surface at night.

Distribution Atlantic, Indian, and Pacific Oceans

Status Not threatened

195

Dories and Allies

The John Dory (*Zeus faber*) is also known as St. Peter's fish. Together with the Cape Dory (*Zeus capensis*) they are the longest of the dories, each growing to a maximum of 36 inches (90 cm).

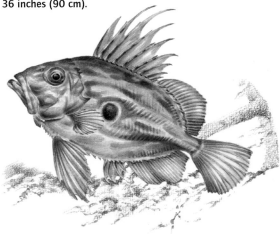

Common name Dories and allies

Families Zeidae (dories), Oreosomatidae (oreos), Caproidae (boarfish)

Order Zeiformes

Number of species Zeidae: 14 in 7 genera; Oreosomatidae: 10 in 4 genera; Caproidae: 12 in 2 genera

Size From around 2.5 in (6.3 cm) to about 36 in (90 cm)

Key features Body highly compressed in all species, very deep in some species; snout pointed to varying degrees; mouth from quite small to extremely large, extendable in all species; large eyes; dorsal fin has spiny front half, soft-rayed back; small strong spines run along both sides of dorsal and anal fins (dories), front dorsal spines very long (John Dory, *Zeus faber*, and others); scales generally small, with sandpaper effect (oreos, boarfish); variable coloration: mottled, silvery-gray to dark, also reds

Breeding Eggs and sperm released into water where they are fertilized; in some species eggs are fertilized inside female, then released; no parental care of eggs or larvae

Diet Fish and invertebrates; also salps (sea squirts)

Habitat Most occur close to seafloor over muddy, sandy, or rocky bottoms, also reefs; a few enter brackish water; all recognized as marine fish; depth from very shallow water, e.g., 16 ft (5 m), to nearly 5,100 ft (1,550 m)

Distribution Antarctic, Atlantic, Indian, and Pacific Oceans, some into major seas like Mediterranean

Status Not threatened

Korean Sand Eel and Tubesnouts

The 7.1-inch (18-cm) tubesnout (*Aulorhynchus flavidus*) is found over sandy or rocky bottoms, eelgrass, or kelp beds in the eastern Pacific. In the breeding season the long snout of the male turns a bright red.

Common name Korean sand eel and tubesnouts

Families Hypoptychidae (sand eel), Aulorhynchidae (tubesnouts)

Order Gasterosteiformes

Number of species 3: Korean sand eel (*Hypoptychus dybowski*), tubenose (*Aulichthys japonicus*), tubesnout (*Aulorhynchus flavidus*)

Size From around 3.4 in (8.5 cm) to 7.1 in (18 cm)

Key features Slim, elongated bodies: scaleless (sand eel), bony plates, or scutes (tubesnouts); pointed snouts (particularly tubenose, tubesnout); eyes relatively large (sand eel), smaller (tubesnout); dorsal and anal fins set well back on body but preceded by up to 26 spines (tubesnout); tail forked; pelvic fin absent in sand eel; coloration: drab, darker above, fading to lighter along belly (sand eel); brownish above, fading to creamy white below, with longitudinal brown band on body (tubesnouts); male tubesnouts turn red during the breeding season

Breeding Eggs laid: in June/July among seaweed in very shallow water (sand eel); in gill chamber of sea squirts (tubenose); in nest built by male among seaweed (tubesnout); male guards eggs until they hatch 2–3 weeks later and protects larvae for short time

Diet Small invertebrates; also fish larvae

Habitat Shallow sandy areas (sand eel) rarely below 66 ft (20 m); shallow water with sandy, rocky, or heavily vegetated bottoms, frequently found in shoals near surface (tubesnout)

Distribution North Pacific from Japan and Korea to Sea of Okhotsk, east of Russia (sand eel), eastern Pacific (tubesnout), and northwest Pacific (tubenose)

Status Not threatened

Sticklebacks

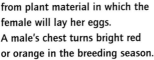

This 4.3-inch (11-cm) male three-spined stickleback (*Gasterosteus aculeatus aculeatus*) constructs a nest from plant material in which the female will lay her eggs. A male's chest turns bright red or orange in the breeding season.

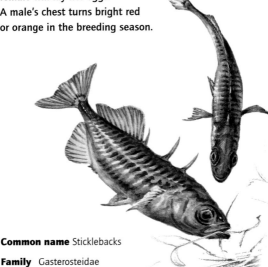

Common name Sticklebacks

Family Gasterosteidae

Order Gasterosteiformes

Number of species 11 in 5 genera

Size From 2 in (5 cm) to 9 in (23 cm)

Key features Elongated, compressed body, with bony plates (scutes) running lengthwise; pointed head; mouth angled upward; eyes relatively large; row of isolated spines running along back and in front of soft dorsal fin; number of spines varies within species, but no spines in Greek nine-spine stickleback (*Pungitius hellenicus*); sometimes pelvic spine and fin lacking; caudal peduncle slim to very slim; coloration: variable, especially in males; blue, green, brown, black, and red (particularly intense during breeding)

Breeding Female lays eggs in nest built by male; young hatch 7–10 days later, protected by male

Diet Invertebrates; also fish eggs, larvae, and small fish

Habitat Pure fresh water through brackish water to fully marine; vegetated areas (preferably with no movement or light currents) and fine-grained bottoms; mostly found in very shallow water, but some occur down to 180 ft (55 m)

Distribution Widely distributed in Northern Hemisphere

Status IUCN lists Greek nine-spine stickleback as Critically Endangered

Seamoths

The pelvic fin spines and rays, together with its midbrown color, help camouflage this 4-inch (10-cm) short dragonfish (*Eurypegasus draconis*)—also called the dwarf seamoth—on the sandy or silty bottoms that it inhabits.

Common name Seamoths

Family Pegasidae

Order Gasterosteiformes

Number of species 5 in 2 genera

Size From 3.7 in (9.5 cm) to 7 in (18 cm)

Key features Body broad and flattened, encased in bony plates; front of head narrower, with prominent eyes; long, flattened, pointed snout; mouth small, located on underside of tip of snout; dorsal and anal fins short; pectoral fins large and winglike; pelvic fins with 1 long spine and few soft rays; tail small, but tail section long and squarish, with projections along its length; coloration variable: mottled brown with overlying netlike pattern to pale to mottled gray; some species capable of color changes; juveniles often differently colored than adults

Breeding Pairs rise off bottom, pressing abdomens (bellies) together and releasing eggs and sperm about 40 in (1 m) above the bottom; eggs float and hatch just over 1 day later

Diet Small invertebrates, usually sucked in from surface of muddy, silty, sandy, or rubbly bottom

Habitat Predominantly marine, but 3 species enter brackish estuaries; usually found at depths of less than 295 ft (90 m); 1 species found at depths of 260–950 ft (80–290 m); rubbly, sandy, silty, or muddy bottoms; sometimes partly buried

Distribution Tropical and temperate regions of Indo-West Pacific

Status IUCN lists brick seamoth (*Pegasus laternarius*) as Vulnerable because of actual or potential levels of harvesting or changes in habitat; concern about other 4 species, listed as Data Deficient

Sea Horses, Pipefish, and Allies

This 1.2-inch (3-cm) long armored stickleback (*Indostomus paradoxus*) can leap out of the water.

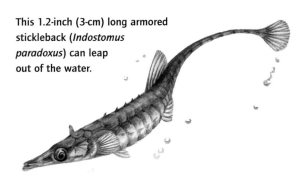

Common name Sea horses, pipefish, and allies

Families Syngnathidae (sea horses, pipefish, pipehorses, seadragons), Solenostomidae (ghost pipefish), Indostomidae (armored sticklebacks)

Subfamilies Syngnathidae: Syngnathinae (pipefish, pipehorses, seadragons); Hippocampinae (sea horses)

Order Gasterosteiformes

Number of species Syngnathidae: around 270 in 52 genera; Solenostomidae: 4 in 1 genus; Indostomidae: 3 in 1 genus

Size From 0.95 in (2.4 cm) to 37.4 in (95 cm)

Key features Elongated body (encased in bony rings or star-shaped plates): held upright (sea horses), or horizontal (pipefish, seadragons); long snout (short in armored sticklebacks), small mouth; 1 to 2 dorsal fins, some with spines and soft rays; some species lack pelvic, caudal, anal fins; long, slim caudal peduncle (armored sticklebacks); varied coloration: muted browns to bright colors; sometimes patterned body or dark bars on fins

Breeding Male carries eggs in belly pouch or mass of spongy tissue (sea horses); female carries eggs in pouch formed by pelvic fin (ghost pipefish)

Diet Invertebrates, worms, and other bottom-dwellers

Habitat Shallow coral reefs, seagrass meadows above 165 ft (50 m) depth or to 310 ft (95 m); some in brackish estuaries; armored sticklebacks in still or slow-moving fresh water, leaf litter on bottom

Distribution Widely distributed in tropical, subtropical, and warm temperate regions of Atlantic, Indian, and Pacific Oceans, and Indo-West Pacific; also Myanmar, Cambodia, Thailand, Mekong Basin

Status IUCN lists 45 sea horse and pipefish species as under threat; sea horse species: 19 Vulnerable, 1 Endangered; pipefish species: 5 Vulnerable, 1 Critically Endangered

Trumpetfish and Cornetfish

The 31-inch (80-cm) Chinese trumpetfish (*Aulostomus chinensis*) lives in the clear, shallow water of coral reefs throughout the Indo-Pacific. It uses both stealth and camouflage to catch unsuspecting prey, such as small fish and shrimp.

Common name Trumpetfish and cornetfish

Families Aulostomidae (trumpetfish), Fistulariidae (cornetfish)

Order Gasterosteiformes

Number of species Aulostomidae: 3 in 1 genus; Fistulariidae: 4 in 1 genus

Size From around 27.5 in (70 cm) to 6.6 ft (2 m)

Key features Extremely elongated body with scales (trumpetfish), naked, or with pricklelike scutes (cornetfish); long heads and snouts (shorter in trumpetfish with single central snout barbel); isolated dorsal spines (trumpetfish); tail either rounded (trumpetfish) or forked with central filament (cornetfish); coloration variable, capable of changing; usually greenish or brownish on back, fading to white along belly, with or without body spotting

Breeding Spawning mainly in spring or summer; eggs scattered in open water, then abandoned; hatching takes several days

Diet Mainly small fish and invertebrates

Habitat Usually associated with reefs but found over range of bottoms; shallow to deeper water

Distribution Tropical and subtropical regions of Indo-Pacific, Eastern Pacific, and Atlantic Oceans

Status Not threatened

Snipefish and Shrimpfish

The extended snout of the 10-inch (25-cm) banded yellowfish (*Centriscops humerosus*) is typical of the family Centriscidae. This fish is found at depths between 115 and 3,280 feet (35–1,000 m).

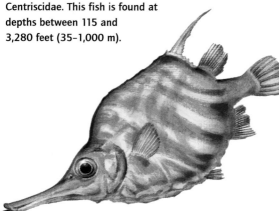

Common name Snipefish, shrimpfish (razorfish), bellowfish, yellowfish

Family Centriscidae

Order Gasterosteiformes

Number of species 13 in 5 genera: *Macroramphosus* (snipefish), *Aeoliscus* and *Centriscus* (shrimpfish/razorfish), *Notopogon* (bellowfish), *Centriscops* (yellowfish)

Size From 6 in (15 cm) to 13.4 in (34 cm)

Key features Body from long and slim (shrimpfish) to deep (snipefish, bellowfish); extended snout; eyes relatively large; body encased in bony plates that form sharp edge along back (snipefish, bellowfish), also belly (shrimpfish); first dorsal fin has 1 long spine and several short ones directed backward in line with back or upward; second dorsal and caudal fin displaced at downward angle (shrimpfish) but lined up more "normally" (snipefish, bellowfish); coloration: silvery with variable lengthwise banding (razorfish); more brilliant coloration, with red, violet, or brown oblique body bands (bellowfish, snipefish)

Breeding Few details available; eggs scattered, then abandoned to float among plankton, where larvae spend some time before migrating toward midwater or bottom

Diet Small invertebrates, including zooplankton

Habitat Shallow to very shallow waters (usually reefs) in tropical regions but may also occur in deeper waters; also some in temperate waters

Distribution Atlantic, Indian, and Pacific Oceans

Status Not threatened

Asian Swamp Eel

Common name Asian swamp eel

Scientific name *Monopterus albus*

Family   Synbranchidae

Order   Synbranchiformes

Size   39 in (1 m)

Key features Snakelike appearance; very small dark eyes; dark
green-brown coloring overall, becoming lighter on
underparts; V-shaped gill opening confined to vicinity of
throat, with small teeth in the mouth; active hunter
feeding on prey both in and out of water

Breeding At any time of year; in some populations all young
hatch as females and breed, turning into males at the
end of their lives; eggs brooded in nests made of saliva
bubbles situated in calm, shallow stretches of water;
female can lay up to 1,000 eggs in a single spawning;
eggs guarded, probably by males, until they hatch;
young remain together in schools at first

Diet   Carnivorous, from worms and amphibians to crustaceans
and fish; can take larger prey that it tears apart by
spinning creature in its jaws

Habitat Occurs natually in shallow water and marshland, as well
as rice paddies in its Asiatic homeland; can move
overland, typically under cover of darkness

Distribution Naturally restricted to parts of eastern and
southeastern Asia extending from northern India; may
also range south to Australia; also introduced and now
spreading in various localities in U.S.

Status   Not threatened

Spiny Eels

The 15-inch (38-cm) lesser spiny eel (*Macrognathus aculeatus*) occurs in medium to large-sized rivers in Asia from Thailand and the Malay Peninsula to Borneo and Indonesia.

Common name Spiny eels

Family Mastacembelidae

Order Mastacembeliformes

Number of species 67 in 4 genera

Size Grows to at least 30 in (75 cm)

Key features Slender, eel-like body with a long, narrow snout; has pectoral fins; dorsal and anal fins extend around tail of body; often blotched coloration helps camouflage them, although may display contrasting bright streaking too; young often differ in coloration and patterning from adults; nocturnal and predatory by nature; solitary, often hiding under rocks and among aquatic vegetation

Breeding Egg laying; breeding pair appears to knot around each other when spawning; produces over 1,000 eggs; no parental care

Diet Worms, small fish, and similar aquatic animals

Habitat Favors slow-flowing streams with vegetation

Distribution From tropical parts of Africa to southern and southeastern Asia

Status IUCN lists *Macrognathus aral* as Data Deficient; most species not believed to be at risk, although local populations may be vulnerable to development or pollution near towns

Gurnards

The large rays of the pectoral fins of this 35.4-inch (90-cm) flying gurnard (*Dactylopterus volitans*) fan out over the sandy bottom as it searches for its favorite meal of crustaceans, especially crabs, clams, and small fish.

Common name Gurnards

Families Dactylopteridae (flying and helmet gurnards), Triglidae (gurnards and sea robins)

Subfamilies Triglidae: Triglinae (gurnards and sea robins): Peristediinae (armored gurnards and armored sea robins)

Order Scorpaeniformes

Number of species Dactylopteridae: 7 in 2 genera; Triglidae: around 150 in 10 genera

Size From 2.8 in (7cm) to 35.4 in (90 cm)

Key features Elongated body tapering toward tail; scutelike scales (helmet gurnards) or spine-covered plates (armored sea robins); head encased; eye ridges (gurnards), or helmetlike structure (flying and helmet gurnards); mouth located under tip of snout, either blunt (helmet gurnards), or 2 projections (gurnards and sea robins); barbels on underside of lower jaw (armored sea robins); 2 dorsal fins in all species; pectorals large and winglike (helmet gurnards) but smaller in others; several free rays in pectoral fin (gurnards); long spine in pelvic fins (helmet gurnards); varied coloration

Breeding Eggs and sperm released late spring or summer, then abandoned

Diet Bottom-dwelling invertebrates; some fish

Habitat Adults marine, juveniles may enter estuaries; helmet gurnards in tropical waters; mostly sandy bottoms; shallow water less than 655 ft (200 m) deep, some species over 2,950 ft (900 m)

Distribution Dactylopteridae: Atlantic and Indo-Pacific Oceans; Triglidae: most temperate and tropical seas: armored sea robins center on Atlantic, Indian, and Pacific Oceans

Status Not threatened

Scorpionfish, Stonefish, and Allies

This 40-inch (100-cm) ocean perch (*Sebastes marinus*) is a popular food fish that is normally trawled in deep waters in the northern reaches on both sides of the Atlantic.

Common name Scorpionfish, stonefish, and allies

Family Scorpaenidae

Subfamilies Sebastinae (rockfish), Scorpaeninae (scorpionfish), Sebastolobinae (thornyheads), Plectrogeninae, Pteroinae (lionfish, turkeyfish, dragonfish, or butterfly cods); Setarchinae, Neosebastinae (gurnard perches); Apistinae, Tetraroginae (waspfish or sailback scorpionfish), Minoinae (stingers), Choridactylinae (ghouls and relatives), Synanceinae (stonefish)

Order Scorpaeniformes

Number of species 380 in about 56 genera

Size From 1.6 in (4 cm) to 40 in (104 cm)

Key features Body elongated and tapering toward tail, usually compressed; head heavy and large with ridges and spines, especially on "cheeks"; eyes and mouth large; fins may carry elongated rays; dorsal, anal, and pelvic fins may have venomous spine glands; varied coloration

Breeding Mostly internal fertilization

Diet Invertebrates; also fish

Habitat Mainly marine; some enter brackish water; mainly shallow water, but some extend down to 6,560 ft (2,000 m)

Distribution All tropical and temperate seas

Status IUCN lists: bocaccio (*Sebastes paucispinis*) as Critically Endangered because of overfishing; shortspine thornyhead (*Sebastolobus alascanus*) and acadian redfish (*Sebastes fasciatus*) as Endangered, also due to overfishing; Saint Helena deepwater scorpionfish (*Pontinus nigropunctatus*) as Vulnerable

Velvetfish

The 2-inch (5-cm) spotted coral croucher (*Caracanthus maculatus*) inhabits crests of shallow coral reefs, with a depth range of between 10 and 50 feet (3–15 m). It occurs from the East Indies north to Japan and through Micronesia.

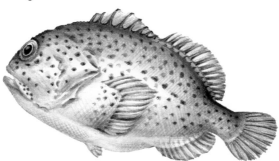

Common name Velvetfish

Families Caracanthidae (orbicular velvetfish or coral crouchers), Aploactinidae (velvetfish), Pataecidae (Australian prowfish), Gnathanacanthidae (red velvetfish), Congiopodidae (pigfish, horsefish, or racehorses)

Order Scorpaeniformes

Number of species Caracanthidae: 5 in 1 genus; Aploactinidae: nearly 40 in about 17 genera; Pataecidae: about 5 in 3 genera; Gnathanacanthidae: 1 in 1 genus; Congiopodidae: 9 in 4 genera

Size From 0.35 in (0.9 cm) to 30 in (76 cm)

Key features Circular or elongated body; head shape variable; mouth frequently directed upward; sometimes spines on cheeks or head; dorsal fin notched or continuous; pelvic fins absent or very small; body scaleless or fully scaled; coloration: bright spots on plain background (orbicular velvetfish); mottled patterning in many velvetfish and pigfish; red blotches and radiating eye streaks on plain background in red velvetfish

Breeding No details available

Diet Wide variety of invertebrates

Habitat Tropical, subtropical, or temperate, even subantarctic (pigfish); all primarily bottom-dwellers: orbicular velvetfish closely associated with branched corals; velvetfish also found over muddy, sandy, or rocky bottoms

Distribution Caracanthidae and Aploactinidae: mainly Indian and Pacific Oceans; other three families: Southern Hemisphere, mainly around Australia, including Tasmania

Status Not threatened

Flatheads

The 12-inch (30-cm) fringelip flathead (*Eurycephalus otaitensis*) buries itself in the sand of lagoon and seaward reefs for camouflage—helped by its mottled pattern and many spines—to wait for a meal of crab and prawns.

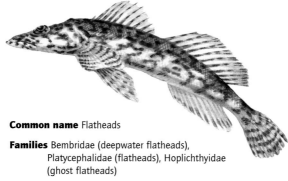

Common name Flatheads

Families Bembridae (deepwater flatheads), Platycephalidae (flatheads), Hoplichthyidae (ghost flatheads)

Order Scorpaeniformes

Number of species Bembridae: 8 in 3 genera; Platycephalidae: about 66 in 18 genera; Hoplichthyidae: 10 or 11 in 1 genus

Size From 2.8 in to 4 ft (1.2 m)

Key features Elongated bodies and flattened heads: least flattened in deepwater flatheads, most flattened in ghost flatheads; pointed snout with large mouth at tip directed upward; body scaleless in ghost flatheads but with line of scutes running length of body; 2 dorsal fins, front spiny and shorter than back; well-formed pectoral and pelvic fins; coloration: reddish in most deepwater flatheads, mottled in most others

Breeding Eggs and sperm scattered into water; eggs take about 1 day to hatch; larvae are planktonic; dusky flathead may be protrandrous hermaphrodite (juveniles are male then female)

Diet Invertebrates and smaller fish

Habitat Deepwater flatheads and ghost flatheads marine; flatheads predominantly marine; most found over sandy or muddy bottoms, sometimes associated with reefs or rocky terrains; some occur in deep to very deep water down to a depth of 4,920 ft (1,500 m)

Distribution Indo-Pacific

Status Not threatened

Greenlings

This 60-inch (1.5-m) lingcod (*Ophiodon elongatus*) has small, pointed teeth interspersed with large, fanglike teeth. Adults feed on crustaceans, octopuses, and squid, the young on copepods.

Common name Greenlings

Family Hexagrammidae

Subfamilies Hexagramminae (greenlings), Pleurogramminae (Atka mackerel), Ophiodontinae (lingcod), Oxylebinae (painted greenling), Zaniolepidinae (combfish)

Order Scorpaeniformes

Number of species 12 in 5 genera

Size From 10 in (25 cm) to 5 ft (1.5 m)

Key features Elongated bodies; head with pointed snout rounded at tip; mouth relatively large; lingcod has large, fanglike teeth separated by smaller teeth; head with cirri; dorsal fin with long base and notch separating front (spinous) part from back (soft-rayed) portion; notch particularly pronounced in combfish, anal fin also long-based; first 2 pelvic fin rays thickened in combfish; coloration: generally mottled and relatively subdued

Breeding Female releases masses of eggs deposited in cracks, on gravel, under rocks or ledges, and guarded by male; may take up to 8 to 10 weeks to hatch; larvae are planktonic for a time

Diet Invertebrates, particularly crustaceans and worms; also sea urchins and fish

Habitat Mainly rocky and sandy areas, often with seaweed such as kelp; shallow (even shoreline) or relatively shallow waters; some species extend to great depths, to nearly 1,900 ft (580 m)

Distribution Northern Pacific Ocean ranging from Alaska southward to Baja California, Mexico

Status Not threatened

Sculpins, Poachers, and Allies

Bullheads (*Cottus gobio*) grow up to 7 inches (18 cm). They feed on bottom-dwelling invertebrates, insects, and crustaceans.

Common name Sculpins, poachers, and allies

Families Cottidae (sculpins), Cottocomephridae (Baikal sculpins), Comephoridae (Baikal oilfish), Abyssocottidae (deep-sea sculpins), Rhamphocottidae (grunt sculpin), Ereuniidae (ereunids), Psychrolutidae (fatheads), Agonidae (poachers), Hemitripteridae (hemitripterids), Bathylutichthyidae (bathylutids)

Order Scorpaeniformes

Number of species Cottidae: about 200 to 300 in around 70 genera; Cottocomephridae: 7 in 3 genera; Comephoridae: 2 in 1 genus; Abyssocottidae: about 23 in 6 genera; Rhamphocottidae: 1 in 1 genus; Ereuniidae: 3 in 2 genera; Psychrolutidae: 40 in 10 genera; Agonidae: 46 in about 17 genera; Hemitripteridae: 9 in 3 genera; Bathylutichthyidae: 1 in 1 genus

Size From 0.8 in (2 cm) to 39 in (99 cm)

Key features Slim, elongated bodies (poachers) or robust (fatheads); head long and pointed (poachers), large and less pointed (Baikal oilfish), or blunt (miller's thumb, *Cottus gobio*, and fatheads); mouth often large; usually 2 dorsal fins, anterior spiny and posterior soft-rayed, but only single dorsal fin (some poachers); dorsal, caudal, and anal joined (Bathylutichthyidae); pectoral fins well formed in most species; pectorals have several free rays (Ereuniidae); varied coloration

Breeding Eggs usually laid on roof of cave and guarded by male; most fertilization external

Diet Fish eggs, numerous invertebrates, and other fish

Habitat Fresh waters in streams, rivers, and lakes, to deep polar waters

Distribution Most seas, including polar regions; predominantly Northern Hemisphere

Status IUCN lists 9 species of Cottidae family as: 2 Data Deficient, 4 Vulnerable, 2 Critically Endangered, 1 Extinct

Lumpfish and Snailfish

The 23.6-inch (60-cm) lumpsucker (*Cyclopterus lumpus*) occurs on both sides of the Atlantic from Canada eastward to Spain.

Common name Lumpfish and snailfish

Families Cyclopteridae (lumpfish, lumpsucker, and lump), Liparidae (snailfish)

Order Scorpaeniformes

Number of species Cyclopteridae: 28 in about 8 genera; Liparidae: 195 in about 19 genera

Size From 0.8 in (2 cm) to 30 in (77 cm)

Key features Stocky, almost globelike bodies (lumpfish) or elongated (snailfish); generally covered in tubercles or lumps (lumpfish), smooth and scaleless (most snailfish); head blunt (lumpfish) or more pointed (snailfish); 2 dorsal fins (lumpfish), front fin covered in skin in subfamily Aptocyclinae, or 1 long-based dorsal fin (snailfish) that can join with caudal and anal fins; in most (but not midwater) species (especially snailfish) pelvic fins joined into suction disk that is located in throat area; variable coloration: often subdued browns and grays (lumpfish), some pale in color (snailfish)

Breeding Eggs are laid in masses on bottom, guarded by male, and hatch in 2 weeks (many lumpfish); eggs laid on bottom or inside gill cavity of crabs (snailfish), some species incubating eggs inside their mouths

Diet Primarily invertebrates, including jellyfish (some lumpfish species); larger species also take fish

Habitat Most species bottom-dwellers over mud, sand, or among gravel, rocks, and seaweed; some shallow-water species found in wave-influenced areas and tidal pools; deepwater species of snailfish at depths over 24,600 ft (7,500 m); some snailfish species also occur in midwater

Distribution Cooler marine waters of Northern Hemisphere extending into polar regions; also widely distributed from Arctic to Antarctic

Status Not threatened

Snooks, Basses, Perches, and Drums

The yellow perch (*Perca flavescens*), native to North American fresh waters, has become widely distributed in the U.S. Length to 20 inches (50 cm).

Common name Snooks, basses, perches, and drums

Families Centropomidae (snooks), Latidae (giant perches), Moronidae (temperate basses), Percichthyidae (temperate perches), Acropomatidae (lantern-bellies and temperate ocean-basses), Serranidae (sea basses), Percidae (freshwater perches), Embiotocidae (surfperches), Glaucosomatidae (pearl perches), Pinguipedidae (sandperches), Sciaenidae (drums or croakers)

Order Perciformes

Number of species Centropomidae: 12 in 1 genus; Latidae: 10 in 3 genera; Moronidae: 4 in 2 genera; Percichthyidae: 25 in 11 genera; Acropomatidae: 40 in 11 genera; Serranidae: 450 in 62 genera; Percidae: 160 in 10 genera; Embiotocidae: 24 in 13 genera; Glaucosomatidae: 4 in 1 genus; Pinguipedidae: 50 in 4 genera; Sciaenidae: 270 in 70 genera (numbers of species are approximate)

Size From 1.7 in (4.3 cm) to over 10 ft (3 m)

Key features Body generally elongate; generally large mouth, mostly at tip of snout but sometimes beneath it; eyes usually large; front part of dorsal fin has hard, undivided spines, back section soft with branched rays; anal fin has spines at front; all fins usually well formed; pelvic fins located below, or slightly in front of, pectorals; coloration variable

Breeding Surfperches livebearers; all other species lay eggs

Diet Small species eat mainly small invertebrates; larger species eat larger invertebrates and fish

Habitat Mainly marine, but some also in brackish and fresh waters; Percichthyidae and Latidae predominantly fresh water; Percidae exclusively fresh water

Distribution Most tropical, subtropical, and temperate waters

Status IUCN lists about 100 species as under various levels of threat

Asiatic Glassfish

Like several other species of glassfish, the highfin glassfish (*Parambassis lala*), also called the Indian glassfish, is a popular aquarium species. Length to 1.2 inches (3 cm).

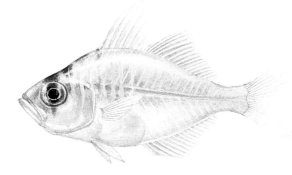

Common Name Asiatic glassfish

Family Ambassidae (Chandidae)

Order Perciformes

Number of species About 49 in 8 genera

Size From 1 in (2.5 cm) to 12 in (30 cm)

Key features Body ranging from oval to more elongated and usually compressed; head pointed, with upward-directed mouth at tip; eyes large; all fins well formed; dorsal fin has pronounced notch, front part with hard spines, back part with soft rays; anal fin not notched but with spiny front part and soft-rayed back part; tail forked; some species almost transparent, with skeleton showing; body frequently has irregular vertical dark bands; larger species frequently silvery

Breeding Males of some species use a zigzag display to entice female; pairs of many species scatter eggs among vegetation and abandon them; in Indian glassfish male builds a nest and guards eggs for about 24 hours until they hatch and then guards young; iridescent glassy perchlet (*Parambassis apogonoides*) reported to be a mouthbrooder in which males incubate eggs

Diet Most species feed on invertebrates; some also take smaller fish; *Paradoxodacna piratica* is a specialized feeder on fish scales

Habitat All waters from clear mountain streams, swamps, ponds, rivers, and lakes to brackish and marine conditions

Distribution Widespread in Asia and Oceania

Status IUCN lists 4 species as Data Deficient

Dottybacks and Allies

All dottybacks and their allies are predatory, but species like the royal gramma (*Gramma loreto*) also feed on the external body parasites of other fish. Length to 3.2 inches (8 cm).

Common name Dottybacks and allies

Families Pseudochromidae (dottybacks), Grammatidae (basslets), Plesiopidae (roundheads), Notograptidae (eel blennies), Opistognathidae (jawfish)

Order Perciformes

Number of species Pseudochromidae: 114 in 17 genera; Grammatidae: about 10 in 2 genera; Plesiopidae: 45 in 11 genera; Notograptidae: 4 in 1 genus; Opistognathidae: 59 in 3 genera

Size From 0.8 in (2 cm) to over 45 in (1.2 m)

Key features Body usually moderately to extremely elongate and eel-like; head usually has relatively large mouth and eyes; mouth bears a central barbel in Notograptidae; dorsal and anal fins long based with spines in front half (*Stalix* species have forked spines in dorsal fin); dorsal, caudal, and anal fins joined in Notograptidae; coloration from drab to bright primary colors

Breeding Generally poorly known; most deposit clumps of eggs on the bottom, which may be defended by the male; some are mouthbrooders; sex changes from female to male occur in some types

Diet Mainly invertebrates

Habitat Mainly shallow or relatively shallow waters, often associated with coral reefs or rubble slopes; few are coastal deepwater species

Distribution All families strictly marine, extending through tropical and subtropical zones of Indo-Pacific, western, and central Atlantic and, in Notograptidae, between southern New Guinea and northern Australia

Status IUCN lists pale dottyback (*Pseudochromis pesi*) as Vulnerable

Sunfish

The green sunfish (*Lepomis cyanellus*) is a native of east and central North America, although it has been introduced elsewhere. Growing to about 12 inches (30 cm), it is a drought-tolerant species found in warm, shallow fresh waters.

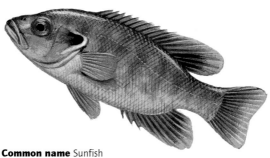

Common name Sunfish

Families Centrarchidae (sunfish), Elassomatidae or Elassomidae (pygmy sunfish)

Order Perciformes

Number of species Centrarchidae: about 30 in 8 genera; Elassomatidae: 6 in 1 genus

Size From about 1.3 in (3.2 cm) to 38 in (97 cm)

Key features Body ranging from relatively elongated to oval shaped; snout pointed in Centrarchidae, rounded in Elassomatidae with mouth at tip; lower jaw longer than upper in more predatory species; eyes relatively large; lateral line usually extends from behind gills to caudal peduncle but absent in pygmy sunfish; all fins well formed; dorsal and anal fin have hard unbranched spines at front, followed by soft branched rays; caudal fin usually forked but rounded in pygmy sunfish; coloration extremely varied

Breeding All Centrarchidae except Sacramento perch (*Archoplites interruptus*) are nest builders; some Elassomatidae scatter eggs and abandon them; others deposit eggs in vegetation, and male guards them until they hatch

Diet Small invertebrates in pygmy sunfish and smaller centrarchids; fish and amphibians in larger species

Habitat Ponds, lakes, creeks, and large rivers, often with overhanging vegetation and overgrown banks; pygmy sunfish favor quiet waters, including swamps and sluggish streams, usually heavily vegetated and with muddy bottoms

Distribution Sunfish widely distributed in North America; some species introduced to numerous locations outside home ranges, including Europe, Africa, Asia, and Caribbean; pygmy sunfish (*Elassoma* spp.) restricted to eastern U.S.

Status IUCN lists 2 species of pygmy sunfish as under threat

Cardinalfish

Like most other cardinalfish, the flamefish (*Apogon maculatus*) tends to remain in, or close to, crevices in near-shore habitats, including reefs, harbors, and sea walls. At night it gathers in large groups to feed on small planktonic invertebrates. Length to 4.3 inches (11 cm).

Common name Cardinalfish

Family Apogonidae

Order Perciformes

Number of species About 295 species in 24 genera

Size From 0.8 in (2 cm) to about 10 in (25 cm)

Key features Body slightly elongated; head and mouth large (particularly in males); eyes large; 2 separate dorsal fins, first with 6–8 hard undivided spines, second with one spine and 8–14 soft rays; anal fin bears 2 spines at front; pelvic fins very large in some species; colors variable but frequently including red or rusty hues; some species, such as pyjama cardinalfish (*Sphaeramia nematoptera*), strikingly marked

Breeding All species whose basic breeding habits are known are paternal mouthbrooders: males retain large-yolked eggs in their mouths until they hatch

Diet Mainly zooplankton and bottom-living invertebrates; feeding occurs mostly at night

Habitat Mostly shallow marine waters, including coral and rocky reefs, harbors, and near sea walls; *Apogon gularis* occurs in relatively deep water at 200–950 ft (60–290 m); several *Apogon* species can be found in brackish water, and all *Glossamia* species occur exclusively in fresh water (mainly in New Guinea)

Distribution Tropical and some subtropical zones of the Pacific, Indian, and Atlantic Oceans, extending into the Mediterranean

Status Not threatened

Remoras and Allies

The sharksucker (*Echeneis naucrates*) is the largest of the remoras, growing to a length of about 43 inches (1.1 m).

Common name Remoras and allies

Families Echeneidae (remoras), Rachycentridae (cobia), Coryphaenidae (dolphinfish)

Order Perciformes

Number of species Echeneidae: 8 in 4 genera; Rachycentridae 1 species; Coryphaenidae 2 in 1 genus

Size From about 12 in (30 cm) to 6.9 ft (2.1 m)

Key features All species elongate; remoras and cobia have flat heads; male dolphinfish have pronounced forehead or crest; eyes large; mouth large; remoras have 2 dorsal fins, the first modified into a sucker; cobia has a long-based, soft dorsal fin preceded by 6–9 isolated short spines; dolphinfish have exceptionally long-based dorsal and anal fins; all other fins well formed, with tail deeply forked in dolphinfish; coloration variable in remoras, ranging from uniform to dark and light longitudinal bands in live sharksucker (*Echeneis naucrates*) and cobia; dolphinfish brilliantly colored in metallic hues

Breeding Eggs scattered in open water and abandoned; larvae of cobia and dolphinfish have spines on their gill covers

Diet All predatory, with remoras feeding mainly on scraps of food from their hosts' meals; cobia and dolphinfish feed on fish, squid, and crustaceans

Habitat All found in open water, with remoras and cobia also in shallower waters in the company of large creatures, including—in the case of remoras—sharks, billfish, and turtles; cobia ranges from the surface down to nearly 4,000 ft (1,200 m); dolphinfish often shelter close to, or beneath, floating objects

Distribution Widespread in Atlantic, Indian, and Pacific Oceans

Status Not threatened

Jacks, Pompanos, and Allies

Occasionally growing up to 4 feet (1.2 m), the crevalle jack (*Caranx hippos*) is a streamlined species often found in shoals around the western Atlantic coast from Novia Scotia to Uruguay. It is fished commercially and for sport, especially around Florida.

Common name Jacks, pompanos, and allies

Families Carangidae (jacks and pompanos), Menidae (moonfish), Leiognathidae (ponyfish, slimys, or slipmouths), Bramidae (pomfrets)

Order Perciformes

Number of species Carangidae: about 146 in 30 genera; Menidae: 1 species; Leiognathidae: about 39 in 3 genera; Bramidae: 21 in 8 genera

Size From 2 in (5 cm) to 6.5 ft (2 m)

Key features Body shape extremely varied (even within families) from elongated and streamlined to deep bodied, but most species oval shaped; head shape variable from pointed, as in the amberjacks (*Seriola* species), to blunt, as in many pomfrets; bony ridges on top of the head in ponyfish; mouth extendable in ponyfish; eyes moderately large; dorsal fin with long base and spines in front section; anal fin similar but with no spine in the moonfish; tail forked; some species lack pelvic fins; coloration generally drab and dark in many pomfrets to silvery and banded in many jacks and pompanos

Breeding Eggs scattered in open water and abandoned

Diet All predatory; smaller and bottom-dwelling species feed mainly on small invertebrates; large species also eat fish

Habitat Mostly open-water shoaling fish, but some, like the moonfish and the lookdowns (*Selene* species), remain closer to the bottom; all species marine, but some may enter brackish water; some species, notably the pilot fish (*Naucrates ductor*) and the golden trevally (*Gnathanodon speciosus*), accompany large fish such as sharks and manta rays

Distribution Widely distributed in Atlantic, Indian, and Pacific Oceans

Status Not threatened

Snappers and Allies

Popular as a game and food fish, the yellowtail snapper (*Ocyurus chrysurus*) ranges from New England to Brazil. It is often found around coral reefs, where it feeds on crustaceans and fish. Length to 34 inches (86 cm).

Common name Snappers and allies

Families Lutjanidae (snappers and fusiliers), Coiidae (tigerfish), Lobotidae (tripletails), Gerreidae (mojarras and silverbiddies), Haemulidae (grunts and sweetlips), Polynemidae (threadfins)

Order Perciformes

Number of species Lutjanidae: about 108 in 19 genera; Coiidae: 5 in 2 genera; Lobotidae: 1 species; Gerreidae: about 50 in 6 genera; Haemulidae: 132 in 18 genera; Polynemidae: 40 in 6 genera

Size From about 2.8 in (7 cm) to 6.6 ft (2 m)

Key features Body varies from moderately elongate in snappers to very elongate in fusiliers and many threadfins; mouth small to relatively large; snout often pointed; eyes relatively large to large; long-based single dorsal fin, with spiny front part in all families except threadfins, which have 2 separate dorsals, the front one spiny, the back one with soft rays; all fins well formed; caudal fin typically forked but straight edged in grunts; pectoral fins in threadfins split into two, with normal upper half but lower half with separate rays; coloration very variable from silvery sided to bold colors

Breeding All believed to be egg scatterers, releasing their eggs either in midwater or over the bottom

Diet Ranges from plankton (fusiliers) to bottom-dwelling invertebrates (many grunts) and fish (tigerfish and many snappers)

Habitat Generally shallow waters, but some snappers found at 1,800 ft (550 m); often found over sandy or rocky bottoms, but many species also found on reefs; some occur in brackish and fresh water

Distribution Widely distributed in most tropical, subtropical, and warm seas

Status IUCN lists mutton snapper (*Lutjanus analis*), Cubera snapper (*L. cyanopterus*) as Vulnerable; brownstriped grunt (*Anisotremus moricandi*) as Endangered

Goatfish and Mullets

The southern goatfish (*Upeneichthys vlamingii*) is found in inshore waters in southern Australia and Tasmania. Goatfish get their name from the whiskerlike barbels under the chin. Length to 13 inches (35 cm).

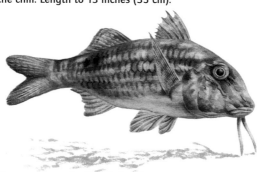

Common name Goatfish and mullets

Family Mullidae

Order Perciformes

Number of species About 60 species in 6 genera

Size From about 3.2 in (8 cm) to about 24 in (61 cm); most species 8–16 in (20–40 cm) long

Key features Body elongate; head with sloping or blunt snout; eyes relatively large; mouth on underside of snout; 2 barbels on chin; 2 dorsal fins, the first with 6–8 spines, the second with a single spine at the front, followed by 8 or 9 soft rays; tail forked; all fins well formed; majority of species brightly colored, often in shades of red; dramatic color changes may occur during mood swings; many species also change color at night

Breeding Very few details known; eggs and sperm released in midwater and abandoned; larvae spend some time in top layers of water column before descending to bottom

Diet Almost exclusively bottom-living invertebrates; some larger species also take smaller fish

Habitat Mainly shallow waters, but a few species, such as west African goatfish (*Pseudapeneus prayensis*), may be found at depths of nearly 1,000 ft (300 m); most species found over sandy or muddy bottoms, but some may also occur on reefs, over rocks, or over seagrass meadows; all species marine, but a few, such as Red Sea goatfish (*Parapeneus forsskali*), may enter brackish waters; some species form large midwater schools in day

Distribution Widely distributed in tropical, subtropical, and to a lesser extent temperate waters in Atlantic, Indian, and Pacific Oceans, extending into many seas, including Mediterranean and Red Sea

Status Not threatened

Porgies and Breams

The common seabream (*Pagrus pagrus*) grows to about 3 feet (91 cm). It is the only member of the family Sparidae under serious threat in the wild, largely due to overfishing.

Common name Porgies and breams

Families Sparidae (porgies), Lethrinidae (emperor breams or scavengers), Nemipteridae (threadfin or whiptail breams)

Order Perciformes

Number of species Sparidae: over 120 in 36 genera; Lethrinidae: about 38 in 5 genera; Nemipteridae: about 63 in 5 genera

Size From about 3.7 in (9.5 cm) to 6.6 ft (2 m)

Key features Ranging from extremely elongate, as in bogue (*Boops boops*), to deep, as in longspine porgy (*Stenotomus caprinus*); head usually robust, with snout ranging from pointed, as in black-streaked monocle bream (*Scolopsis taeniatus*), to very blunt, as in musselcracker seabream (*Sparodon durbanensis*); eyes usually large; 1 dorsal fin with spiny front part; anal fin with several spines at front; all fins well formed; variable coloration, often including reflective scales; few species with contrasting coloration, such as black and silver

Breeding Eggs scattered and abandoned; sex changes frequent in all families

Diet Most predatory, taking prey ranging from zooplankton to fish and frequently including crabs, mollusks, and other hard-shelled invertebrates; some species almost exclusively herbivorous, feeding mainly on marine algae

Habitat Most occur at shallow to moderate depths of less than 330 ft (100 m); some range to depths of about 1,310 ft (400 m); habitats vary from sandy to rocky or rubbly, while some are found on coral reefs or seagrass meadows

Distribution Tropical, subtropical, and temperate Atlantic, Indian, and Pacific Oceans

Status IUCN lists common seabream (*Pagrus pagrus*) as Endangered

Monos and Scats

The silver mono (*Monodactylus argenteus*) is also known as the mono, silver moony, or fingerfish. It frequents mangroves, estuaries, creeks, and coastal reefs, and may enter fresh water. Length to 10 inches (25 cm).

Common name Monos and scats

Families Monodactylidae (monos, moonfish, or fingerfish), Scatophagidae (scats)

Order Perciformes

Number of species Monodactylidae: 4 in 2 genera; Scatophagidae: 4 in 1 genus

Size From about 3.2 in (8.3 cm) to 16 in (40 cm)

Key features Both families deep bodied and laterally flattened; in monos dorsal and anal fins have long bases and pointed tips; in scats fins are more rounded, with stout spines with venomous glands in front half and a deep notch between front and back portions; pelvic fins of monos are lost (or nearly so) as juveniles mature; caudal fin slightly forked in monos and straight edged or slightly rounded in scats; coloration generally silvery in monos, with colored fins; juveniles darker than adults; silvery in most scats, with bands and spots on the body

Breeding No details available for monos, but all species believed to spawn at sea and abandon their eggs; all species of scat believed to breed at sea, except the scatty or African scat (*Scatophagus tetracanthus*)

Diet Monos feed mainly on invertebrates and small fish; scats more wide ranging, feeding on invertebrates, algae, and detritus, including feces and sewage

Habitat Both families live mainly in brackish conditions such as mangrove swamps and in the sea; both also occasionally travel into fresh waters, particularly during juvenile stages, especially scatty or African scat, which is frequently found in rivers and lagoons in East Africa

Distribution Widely distributed in the Indo-Pacific

Status Not threatened

Archerfish

At 16 to 18 inches (40–45 cm) in length the largescale archerfish (*Toxotes chatareus*) is the largest member of the family Toxotidae.

Common name Archerfish

Family Toxotidae

Order Perciformes

Number of species 6 in 1 genus

Size From about 6 in (15 cm) to 18 in (46 cm)

Key features Body deep and flattened from side to side, although less so in primitive archerfish (*Toxotes lorentzi*); head sharply pointed with flat top; large mouth directed upward at an angle; eyes very large and close to top of head; top of body forms straight line from tip of snout to front of dorsal fin; dorsal and anal fins have a few spines at the front, followed by soft, branched rays; tail, pectoral, and pelvic fins well formed; all species except primitive archerfish basically silver bodied with dark bands or blotches along top half; primitive archerfish lacks the bold black blotches; dorsal and anal fins may be dusky with some yellow, particularly in smallscale archerfish (*T. microlepis*)

Breeding Very few details available, but largescale archerfish (*T. chatareus*) reported to lay between 20,000 and 150,000 eggs, in either fresh or brackish water

Diet Mainly insects and other invertebrates, frequently, but not always, knocked off foliage with water drops; also smaller fish; largescale and common archerfish (*T. jaculatrix*) eat some plant matter

Habitat Predominantly marine, but all species spend periods in fresh water, especially the smallscale, primitive, and western archerfish (*T. oligolepis*)—these species frequently found in swamps and streams, often with overhanging vegetation; common and largescale archerfish typically found in brackish mangrove swamps and estuaries

Distribution From India to the Philippines, Australia, and Polynesia

Status Not threatened

Butterflyfish

The 8-inch (20-cm) copperband or beaked butterflyfish (*Chelmon rostratus*) is found in the Indian and Pacific Oceans.

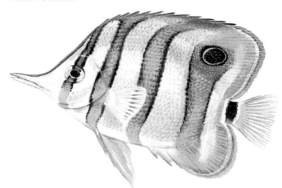

Common name Butterflyfish

Family Chaetodontidae

Order Perciformes

Number of species About 128 in 11 genera

Size From 3 in (7.6 cm) to 12 in (30 cm); most species 4.7–10 in (12–25 cm)

Key features Body flattened from side to side and usually quite deep; head pointed, particularly in species that extract food from crevices or polyps; small mouth at tip of snout; dorsal fin with spiny front section and soft-rayed back; anal fin with 3–5 spines at front; all fins well formed; body scales extend onto both dorsal and anal fins; most species brightly colored, often with vertical bands; eye frequently hidden by a vertical band or patch; false eyes or eye-spots common on either body or back lower edge of the dorsal fin; many species develop night colors that differ from the day ones; colors of juveniles frequently different

Breeding Eggs released into water and unprotected; hatch in 18–30 hours; larvae have distinctive bony plates during free-swimming planktonic stage, which may last from a few weeks to several months

Diet Most feed on small invertebrates, coral polyps or tentacles, zooplankton, algae, or fish eggs; some species very specialized feeders

Habitat Mainly found in water less than 65 ft (20 m) deep, mostly on coral reefs; some species in rubble zones and water down to 656 ft (200 m)

Distribution Tropical and subtropical Indo-Pacific plus warm-temperate Atlantic

Status IUCN lists 5 *Chaetodon* species as Vulnerable

Angelfish

The regal angelfish (*Pygoplites diacanthus*) of the Indo-Pacific grows to about 10 inches (25 cm) in length. Often found near caves, it feeds on sponges and other small invertebrates. It may appear in shoals or solitarily.

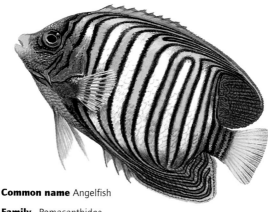

Common name Angelfish

Family Pomacanthidae

Order Perciformes

Number of species About 85 in 7 genera

Size From 2.4 in (6 cm) to 24 in (60 cm)

Key features Body strongly flattened from side to side and usually quite deep; head blunt to slightly pointed; small mouth located at tip of snout; bone in front of gill cover carries a stout spine; dorsal fin has spiny front section and soft-rayed back section; anal fin has 3 spines at the front and soft-rayed back section; all other fins well formed; striking coloration in many species, particularly in pygmy angels; juveniles often have completely different coloration and patterning than adults

Breeding Eggs released into water while spawning above the reef and then abandoned; hatching may take 18–30 hours; larvae have spiny scales (but not bony plates) and are planktonic for a while

Diet *Centropyge* species feed mainly on algae; *Genicanthus* species prefer zooplankton; most other species feed on sea squirts, sponges, soft corals, sea pens, other invertebrates, and algae

Habitat Most species found on shallow-water tropical reefs; a few, such as the masked angelfish (*G. personatus*), are found in deeper water; angelfish are very rarely found in open sandy areas

Distribution Widely distributed in all tropical seas, with nearly 90 percent of species in Indo-Pacific

Status IUCN lists resplendent angelfish (*C. resplendens*) as Vulnerable

Old Wife and Armorheads

The old wife (*Enoplosus armatus*) can grow to nearly 20 inches (50 cm) but is usually about half that size. It is primarily a shallow-water species.

Common name Old wife and armorheads

Families Enoplosidae (old wife), Pentacerotidae (armorheads or boarfish)

Order Perciformes

Number of species Enoplosidae: 1 species; Pentacerotidae: 14 in 8 genera

Size From 9.5 in (24 cm) to 39 in (1m)

Key features Deep, compressed body; pointed head; large eyes; armorheads have bony plates on head; old wife has 2 dorsal fins, the first spiny, the second sickle-shaped with 1 spine followed by long, soft rays; armorheads have 1 dorsal fin with spiny front section; anal fin also bears spines; pelvic fins large; old wife has bold, vertical black bands on a silvery background, with one band passing through the eye; armorhead coloration varied, including some striped species, others more evenly colored

Breeding Very little information, but floating eggs are scattered and abandoned

Diet Old wife feeds mainly on bottom-living invertebrates, including worms and crustaceans; armorheads also tend to feed off the bottom, with some species including brown algae, brittlestars, and other starfish in their diet

Habitat Old wife found mainly in estuaries, coastal waters, reefs, and seagrass beds; armorheads range from very shallow water, such as rocky reefs, to relatively deep water along the edge of the continental shelf

Distribution Old wife: southern half of Australia; armorheads: southwestern Atlantic and Indo-Pacific

Status Not threatened

Chameleon Fish and Leaffish

The Amazon leaffish (*Monocirrhus polyacanthus*) is an efficient predator that uses its leaflike appearance to drift close to unsuspecting prey. Length to 3.2 inches (8 cm).

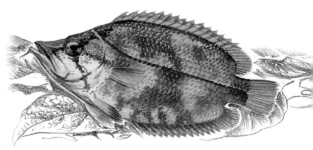

Common name Chameleon fish, leaffish, and pikehead

Families Badidae, Nandidae, Luciocephalidae

Order Perciformes

Number of species Badidae (chameleon fish): 15 in 2 genera; Nandidae (leaffish): about 8 in 4 genera; Luciocephalidae (pikehead): 1 species

Size From about 1.9 in (4.8 cm) to 8.3 in (21 cm)

Key features Body elongate in chameleon fish, deeper and more compressed in leaffish; mouth large to very large in most species except chameleon fish; head pointed; eyes medium to large; dorsal fin has long base occupying most of back, with front half armed with spines; rounded tail; lateral line incomplete or missing; coloration: most leaffish mottled shades of brown and tan; chameleon fish extremely variable, with colorful fins, body spots, and patches that change rapidly according to mood

Breeding Common chameleon fish (*Badis badis*) lays up to 100 eggs in a cave where male guards them until they hatch after about 3 days; Amazon leaffish (*Monocirrhus polyacanthus*) and Guyana leaffish (*Polycentrus schomburgkii*) lay up to 300 or 600 eggs respectively on a leaf, and male guards them for about 4 days until they hatch; eggs of *Nandus* species (and probably others) scattered and abandoned

Diet Ranges from small invertebrates to sizable fish

Habitat Common, Bornean (*N. nebulosus*), and Guyana leaffish occur in fresh and brackish water; other species exclusively in fresh water, in wide range of habitats from ditches and swamps to streams, rivers, and pools

Distribution Amazon and Guyana leaffish: northeastern South America; *Afronandus* and *Polycentropsis* spp: tropical West Africa; *Nandus* spp: Pakistan to Borneo; chameleon fish widely distributed in Pakistan and Burma

Status Not threatened

Climbing Perches and Bushfish

The climbing perch (*Anabas testudineus*) gets its name because it is sometimes found among the branches of trees. However, it probably simply gets stranded there during floods. Length to 10 inches (25 cm).

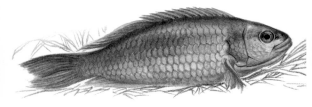

Common name Climbing perches and bushfish

Family Anabantidae

Order Perciformes

Number of species About 30 in 4 genera

Size From about 3.2 in (8 cm) to 10 in (25 cm)

Key features Climbing perches (*Anabas* spp.) and kurpers (*Sandelia* spp.) elongate and almost cylindrical at front; bushfish (*Ctenopoma, Microctenopoma* spp.) more varied, ranging from elongated to deeper bodied; eyes large; mouth medium to large on tip of often pointed snout, frequently pointing slightly upward; dorsal and anal fins have long bases; powerful tail; coloration very varied, ranging from drab and darkish in climbing perches and kurpers to broadly banded and colorful in orange bushfish (*Ctenopoma ansorgii*) or boldly spotted as in leopard bushfish (*C. acutirostre*)

Breeding *Anabas* and *Microctenopoma* species build small bubble nests, and up to 5,000 eggs may be guarded by male until hatching in 1–2 days; *Ctenopoma* spp. free spawning, releasing many eggs (up to 20,000 in *C. kingsleyae*) that rise to surface and hatch in 1–2 days; *Sandelia* spp. lay up to 7,000 sticky eggs on small area of bottom cleared by male, which guards them until they hatch 2 days later

Diet Climbing perches take wide range of animal and plant matter; others more exclusively predatory, taking invertebrates and small fish

Habitat Wide range of still or slow-flowing fresh waters, including paddy fields, pools, and marshes

Distribution *Anabas* spp.: widely from India to the Philippines, introduced to Papua New Guinea; *Ctenopoma* and *Microctenopoma* spp.: widely in Africa south of Sahara; *Sandelia* spp.: exclusively in South Africa

Status IUCN lists Eastern Province rocky (*Sandelia bainsii*) as Endangered

Gouramis

The 2.5 inch (6.5-cm) Siamese fighting fish (*Betta splendens*) is a popular aquarium fish. It is famed not only for the aggressive disputes between males but also for its bubble-nest building and the magnificent fins of cultured varieties.

Common name Gouramis

Families Helostomatidae, Osphronemidae, Belontiidae

Order Perciformes

Number of species About 90 in 14–15 genera

Size From about 1 in (2.5 cm) to 30 in (76 cm)

Key features Body ranges from slim-bodied, pointed-snout species such as licorice (*Parosphromenus* spp.) and croaking gouramis (*Trichopsis* spp.) to oval-shaped, round-snouted species such as giant gourami (*Osphronemus* spp.); teeth lacking in jawbones of some species; eyes usually relatively large; most species have filamentlike elongations on pelvic fins, most pronounced in *Osphronemus*, *Colisa*, and *Trichogaster* spp. but totally lacking in kissing gourami (*Helostoma temminckii*); dorsal fin narrow based in fighters, croakers, *Trichogaster* spp, and pointed-tail gourami (*Malpulatta kretseri*); considerably wider in others, particularly *Colisa* spp. and kissing gourami; tail ranges from pointed to almost straight; coloration very variable, more pronounced in males than females

Breeding Bubble-nesting species build nests on water surface or under overhang or submerged leaf; mouthbrooding species incubate eggs inside mouth of one parent

Diet Plants and animals, particularly small invertebrates

Habitat Wide range of still waters, often with overhanging and submerged vegetation; includes waters that may become depleted of oxygen for part of year; some species, e.g., pointed-tail gourami, found in secluded flowing waters

Distribution Widely distributed in Southeast Asia, India, Pakistan, Thailand, and Malay Archipelago

Status IUCN lists 14 species as under threat

Snakeheads

The striped or chevron snakehead (*Channa striata*) is one of the largest species, growing to about 39 inches (1 m) long. Like other snakeheads, it is highly predatory.

Common name Snakeheads

Family Channidae

Order Perciformes

Number of species About 31 in 2 genera

Size From 6 in (15 cm) to 6 feet (1.8 m)

Key features Elongate, almost cylindrical body; large, blunt-snouted, snakelike head; large scales on top of head; large mouth with lower jaw slightly longer than upper jaw; large eyes; dorsal and anal fins both have long bases extending along most of back and more than half the belly respectively; tail well formed and rounded; no spines on any fins; coloration variable, with smaller species and juveniles generally more colorful than adults

Breeding Most species produce floating eggs; some produce floating nests of weeds and leaves; parental care typical of most species, with some guarding their young for up to a month; at least 1 species, the Ceylon snakehead (*Channa orientalis*), is a mouthbrooder

Diet Mainly invertebrates, including worms, insects, and crustaceans; all species also take fish; some plants may be consumed

Habitat Wide range of still and slow-flowing fresh waters, such as streams, rivers, canals, ditches, ponds, swamps, and marshes, including waters that seasonally dry up

Distribution *Channa* species widely distributed throughout southern Asia, mainly in India, Indonesia, Malaysia, Thailand, and China, with *C. argus* extending into Russia; introduced to several countries, ranging from U.S. to Madagascar; *Parachanna* species widely found in tropical Africa

Status Not threatened

Hawkfish

The scarlet hawkfish (*Neocirrhites armatus*) is found in the Pacific Ocean, where it frequents reefs and submarine terraces. It is highly predatory and grows to about 35.5 inches (90 cm).

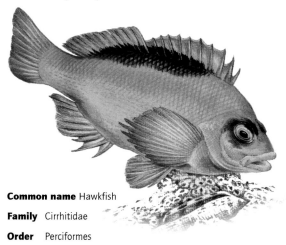

Common name Hawkfish

Family Cirrhitidae

Order Perciformes

Number of species 30–35 in 12 genera

Size From about 2.8 in (7 cm) to 24 in (60 cm); possibly up to 39 in (1 m)

Key features Body moderately elongated; head slightly to sharply pointed; mouth from small to moderately large; large eyes; dorsal fin with 10 spines in the front section and soft rays behind; spines with hairy looking tufts (cirri) on tips; all fins well formed; coloration variable but often bright

Breeding Single male mates with a harem of several females; eggs released into the water during nightly spawnings and abandoned

Diet Most species feed on crustaceans and other invertebrates; many species also take smaller fish

Habitat Mainly shallow-water rocky and coral reefs, especially where there are long-branched hard corals; most species at depths of less than 80 ft (25 m), but dwarf hawkfish (*Cirrhitichthys falco*) ranges to depths of 150 ft (46 m)

Distribution Widely distributed in tropical zones of the Atlantic, Indian, and Pacific Oceans, with most species occurring in the Indo-Pacific

Status Not threatened

Cichlids

The blue-white labido (*Labidochromis caeruleus*) comes from the northwestern coast of Africa's Lake Malawi. The eggs are brooded in the females' mouths, and the fry also retreat there at any sign of danger. Length to 3.2 inches (8 cm).

Common name Cichlids

Family Cichlidae

Order Perciformes

Number of species Probably over 2,000 in over 105 genera

Size From 1.5 in (3.5 cm) to about 36 in (90 cm)

Key features Mostly oval but ranging from almost circular in discus (*Symphysodon* spp.) to slim and elongate in pike cichlids (*Crenicichla* spp.); head rounded to pointed, with small lips or large fleshy ones; teeth usually brown-tipped but vary in shape according to diet; eyes usually quite large; front half of dorsal fin has hard, unbranched spines, back half has soft, branched rays; anal fin similar but with shorter base; caudal fin well formed; coloration very variable—males usually more colorful

Breeding Adults typically protect eggs and young; some are substrate spawners, laying eggs on specially prepared sites such as rocks, leaves, or snail shells; some are mouthbrooders—males attract females to the spawning sites, and females incubate the eggs in their mouths

Diet Most eat a wide range of animals, although many also eat plants; specialized feeders graze on algae and microorganisms, some on scales or eyes of other fish

Habitat From shallow, shaded forest streams and deep, wide rivers to estuaries, marshes, lakes, and backwaters; most occur in fresh water

Distribution Central and South America, southern U.S., West Indies, African rift lakes (Malawi, Tanganyika, Victoria, and others), tropical Africa, India, Sri Lanka, Syria, Israel, Iran, Madagascar

Status IUCN lists 154 species as under various levels of threat

Damselfish

The western Pacific tomato clownfish (*Amphiprion frenatus*) is an anemonefish—a species that hides among anemones. Length to 5.5 inches (14 cm).

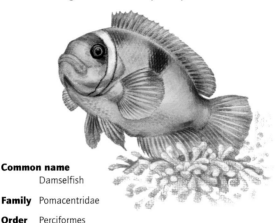

Common name
Damselfish

Family Pomacentridae

Order Perciformes

Number of species About 335 in 28 genera

Size From about 1.6 in (4 cm) to 14 in (36 cm); most species 3.2–4.7 in (8–12 cm)

Key features Body relatively deep; almost cylindrical in many midwater plankton feeders; some species quite elongate; head often blunt in species living near bottom, less so in midwater species; mouth usually small; eyes relatively large; dorsal fin with long base and hard spines along most of length; tail forked; coloration ranging from bright in anemonefish to subdued in many more mobile swimmers; juveniles of drab species often colorful

Breeding Eggs laid on precleaned surface, usually under cover or close to base of host anemone; in Garibaldi (*Hypsypops rubicundus*) nest is patch of red algae; intense courtship by male precedes egg laying; in some, such as *Chromis* and *Dascyllus*, single male may spawn with several females; eggs guarded mainly by male; hatching takes 2–7 days depending on species

Diet Mainly small invertebrates; many species also feed on algae; a few feed on coral polyps

Habitat Mostly shallow water on or near coral reefs; some live on sandy or rocky bottoms at less than 65 ft (20 m); a few *Chromis* species occur down to 330 ft (100 m); a few species found in fresh water and brackish mangroves and estuaries

Distribution All tropical seas and some warm-temperate regions, e.g., off California and around Australia and New Zealand

Status IUCN lists St. Helena chromis (*Chromis sanctaehelenae*), St. Paul's Gregory (*C. sanctipauli*), and St. Helena Gregory (*Stegastes sanctaehelenae*) as Vulnerable

Wrasses

The clown coris (*Coris aygula*) feeds mainly on hard-shelled invertebrates such as mollusks and sea urchins. It is sometimes caught commercially and as a game fish. The specimen shown here is a juvenile, complete with false eyes on its fins. Length to 4 feet (1.2 m).

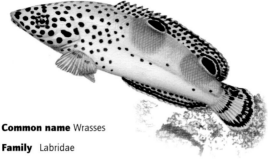

Common name Wrasses

Family Labridae

Order Perciformes

Number of species 450–500 in more than 60 genera

Size From about 1.8 in (4.5 cm) to over 8 ft (2.5 m); majority of species 6–8 in (15–20 cm)

Key features Mostly relatively elongated, with some, such as cleaner wrasses, slim and almost cylindrical in cross-section; many larger species deeper-bodied; head usually pointed; extendable jaw; forward-pointing front teeth, usually with gap between; all fins well formed; front part of dorsal and anal fin have hard, unjointed spines (more in dorsal than anal), followed by soft, branched rays; body scales cycloid; coloration very diverse and usually much more intense in males than females

Breeding Spawning occurs in pairs or shoals; males and females swim together from the reef toward surface, releasing eggs and sperm into water; eggs float to the surface, where they hatch

Diet Predatory; smaller species feed primarily on invertebrates; larger species also feed on other fish; specialized feeders include cleaner wrasses that feed on external parasites of other fish; some larger wrasses feed on toxic organisms such as seastars, urchins, boxfish, and seahares

Habitat Tropical, temperate, and subarctic coastal waters, preferring rocky and reef habitats

Distribution Widely distributed in the Atlantic, Indian, and Pacific Oceans and most seas, including the Mediterranean and Red Sea

Status IUCN lists 6 species as under various levels of threat, including the giant wrasse (*Cheilinus undulatus*) as Endangered

Parrotfish

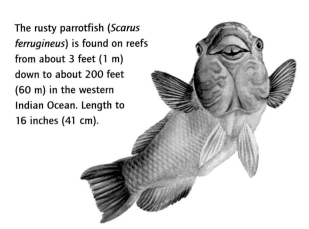

The rusty parrotfish (*Scarus ferrugineus*) is found on reefs from about 3 feet (1 m) down to about 200 feet (60 m) in the western Indian Ocean. Length to 16 inches (41 cm).

Common name Parrotfish

Family Scaridae

Order Perciformes

Number of species About 94 species in 10 genera

Size From about 5 in (13 cm) to about 51 in (1.3 m); most species are 12–20 in (30–50 cm)

Key features Body often elongated oval shape; some of smallest species somewhat slimmer, while green humphead (*Bolbometopon muricatum*) is deeper just behind head; head usually tapers to rounded snout, but green humphead has high, bulbous forehead; teeth fused to form prominent parrotlike beak; all fins well formed; dorsal and anal fins have hard, unbranched, pointed spines at the front (many more in dorsal than anal), followed by soft, branched rays; pelvic fin has prominent spine at front; caudal fin may have extended top and bottom rays; body scales usually large and cycloid

Breeding Most individuals change sex as they mature; in initial mature phase most are drab breeding females with a few drab primary males; in next (terminal) phase females become brightly colored secondary males, some of which become dominant, although some primary males will mate

Diet Most species herbivorous; most also take in coral fragments that are ground up in the gut to crush algal cells and make them digestible; a few species are live coral eaters

Habitat Most species found on coral reefs; a few may occur in seagrass meadows and on rocky reefs

Distribution Mostly tropical Atlantic, Indian, and Pacific Oceans, Red Sea, Caribbean, plus a few species in Mediterranean

Status IUCN lists rainbow parrotfish (*Scarus guacamaia*) as Vulnerable

Blennies

The 12-inch (30-cm) shanny (*Lipophrys pholis*) lives in the temperate eastern Atlantic, where it frequents shallow rocky coasts. Food consists mainly of mollusks, barnacles, and algae.

Common name Blennies (combtooth blennies)

Family Blenniidae

Order Perciformes

Number of species Nearly 350 in about 53 genera

Size From less than 1.2 in (3 cm) to about 21.3 in (54 cm); most species less than 6 in (15 cm) long

Key features Body elongate, especially in the hairtail blenny (*Xiphasia setifer*) and the Japanese snake blenny (*X. matsubarai*); body scaleless; head usually blunt, but sabre-toothed blennies have pointed snouts; mouth located on underside of snout; teeth in comblike arrangement; most species have elongated "canine" teeth on side of jaw; eyes usually large; tufts frequently present on nostrils, above or between eyes, or on nape; dorsal and anal fins long based; dorsal fin may have notch between hard-spined front part and soft-rayed back part; caudal fin may have top and bottom extensions; pelvic fins have short, embedded spine and are farther forward on body than pectorals; most species mottled in browns and creams but some brightly colored

Breeding Males may spawn with several females in some species; eggs laid in caves, crevices, or empty snail shells and are guarded by the male

Diet Mostly algae and small invertebrates; species with specialized diets include scale-eating blenny and cleaner mimics

Habitat Nearly all marine, occurring in shallow or very shallow waters; some, like butterfly blenny (*Blennius ocellaris*), found at depths of about 330 ft (100 m); preferred habitats are rocky bottoms, tidal pools, and reefs

Distribution Widely distributed in tropical, subtropical, and temperate Atlantic, Indian, and Pacific Oceans

Status Not threatened

Gobies

The 4.5-inch (11-cm) sand goby (*Pomatoschistus minutus*) lives in temperate brackish or marine waters, where it feeds mainly on marine worms and crustaceans.

Common name Gobies

Families Gobiidae (gobies), Eleotridae (sleeper gobies, sleepers, or gudgeons), Rhyacichthyidae (loach gobies)

Order Perciformes

Number of species Gobiidae: 2,000 in about 212 genera; Eleotridae: about 150 in 35 genera; Rhyacichthyidae: about 92 in about 21 genera

Size From 0.3 in (7.6 mm) to about 28 in (71 cm); most species are between 3–8 in (7.5–20 cm)

Key features Body elongate and often almost cylindrical in cross-section; mouth usually large, often with fleshy lips; eyes near top of head; first dorsal fin with hard, unbranched spines and second with soft, branched rays; pelvic fins may form sucker (gobies) or range from free to almost fused (sleepers); tail usually rounded; coloration variable—many bottom-living species cryptically mottled, others brilliantly colored, with first dorsal fin frequently colorful in males

Breeding Eggs usually laid on precleaned site such as a rock or roof of a cave and guarded by male

Diet Most feed on invertebrates; midwater species usually feed on plankton; larger species may also eat smaller fish

Habitat Most occur either in brackish or marine conditions; some occur in fresh water; many can tolerate wide salinity range; exceptional habitats include fast-flowing mountain streams, caves, and tidal mudflats; some form associations with totally unrelated creatures like sea urchins and shrimp

Distribution Mainly in tropical and temperate regions; only a few species found in cooler waters

Status IUCN lists 58 gobies and 4 sleeper gobies as threatened; 5 are Critically Endangered, including Elizabeth Springs goby (*Chlamydogobius micropterus*) and dwarf pygmy goby (*Pandaka pygmaea*); 17 species are listed as Vulnerable

Surgeonfish

The Achilles tang (*Acanthurus achilles*) from the tropical Pacific region lives on shallow reefs. It feeds on stringlike and fleshy algae that grow on the reefs and rocks. Length to 9.5 inches (24 cm).

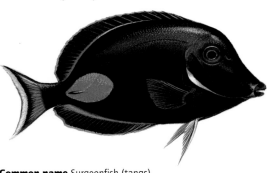

Common name Surgeonfish (tangs)

Family Acanthuridae

Order Perciformes

Number of species About 84 in 7 genera

Size From 4.7 in (12 cm) to 39 in (1 m); most species 8–14 in (20–35 cm)

Key features Body oval and compressed; head generally pointed, with hornlike growth in many unicornfish; small mouth located at tip of snout; eyes high on head; long-based dorsal and anal fins with spiny front portion in both but with fewer spines in anal fin; all fins well formed, with tail usually slightly forked; caudal peduncle narrow and bearing bladelike spines in most species but not in *Naso* and *Prionurus* species that have plates rather than spines; coloration varied, ranging from dull almost uniform hues to the brilliant colors of some species; juveniles of some species look quite different than adults

Breeding Spawning may occur in pairs or groups, and eggs are scattered in open water; eggs float and hatch as rapidly as 24 hours in some species; newly hatched larvae almost transparent and diamond shaped, with large eyes, triangular heads, and long spines on fins; larvae spend some time among plankton, only drifting down to reef once they begin to change into the adult form

Diet Most species feed mainly on algae or zooplankton

Habitat Most species closely associated with shallow-water coral reefs, but larger species are found in deeper water down to 195 ft (60 m) on outer reef dropoffs

Distribution Widely distributed in all tropical and subtropical seas but absent from Mediterranean

Status Not threatened

Barracudas

At 12 inches (30 cm) in length the yellowstripe barracuda (*Sphyraena chrysotaenia*) of the Indo-Pacific and Mediterranean is a relatively small species.

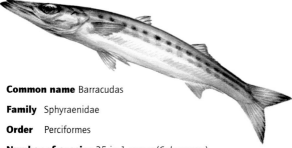

Common name Barracudas

Family Sphyraenidae

Order Perciformes

Number of species 25 in 1 genus (*Sphyraena*)

Size From about 12 in (30 cm) to 6.7 ft (2.1 m); at least half of all species grow to over 39 in (1 m)

Key features All species elongated with pointed head and forked tail; mouth large with numerous, powerful fanglike teeth; lower jaw slightly longer than upper jaw; large eyes; two widely separated dorsal fins; most fins except tail relatively small; lateral line well developed; coloration usually includes dark blue on back, shading to silvery along the belly; body often attractively marked with vertical bands; fins may be colored

Breeding Spawning usually occurs in groups in open water; eggs scattered and abandoned; few other details known

Diet Almost exclusively fish, including smaller barracuda and squid; many smaller species also regularly eat shrimp

Habitat Frequently found near the surface but may descend to depths of about 330 ft (100 m); may be found close to shore, in harbors and lagoons, or in open seas; young may enter brackish water around estuaries and mangroves

Distribution Widespread in tropical and subtropical Atlantic, Indian, and Pacific Oceans

Status Not threatened

Mackerels and Tunas

The Atlantic mackerel (*Scomber scombrus*) is one of the world's most important commercial fish species. Many thousands of tons are caught each year. Length to 24 inches (60 cm).

Common name Mackerels and tunas

Family Scombridae

Order Perciformes

Number of species About 54 species in 15 genera

Size From about 8 in (20 cm) to 15 ft (4.6 m)

Key features Body spindle shaped and almost cylindrical in cross-section; head pointed; large eyes halfway between back of upper jaw and top of head; first dorsal fin with hard spines; both fins fit into grooves when folded back; pectoral fins with hard leading edge; finlets behind 2nd dorsal and anal fins extend to base of tail; tail lunate with hard, stiff leading edge; 2 keels on either side of caudal peduncle; scales very small; most species have blue backs and silvery bellies; bonitos usually have longitudinal stripes on body; mackerels usually have spots or dark streaks on upper half of body

Breeding All are egg scatterers; a northern bluefin tuna (*Thunnus thynnus*) weighing 600–660 lb (270–300 kg) can produce 10 million eggs in a single spawning; skipjack tuna (*Katsuwonus pelamis*) may breed all year in tropics; others such as northern bluefin have narrow spawning seasons; southern bluefin tuna (*T. maccoyii*) may spawn only once in a lifetime; hatching may take as little as 3 days

Diet Mostly smaller fish, squid, and crustaceans; some smaller species also sift zooplankton

Habitat Open water, frequently near surface but some down to about 820 ft (250 m); a few, notably the albacore (*T. alalunga*), may descend to about 1,970 ft (600 m)

Distribution Widely distributed in tropical and subtropical seas; some species are restricted, such as the Monterey Spanish mackerel (*Scomberomorus concolor*), which is endemic to the northern part of the Gulf of California

Status IUCN lists 5 species as under various levels of threat, including southern bluefin tuna as Critically Endangered

Swordfish and Marlins

At about a maximum length of 16.4 feet (5 m) the Atlantic blue marlin (*Makaira nigricans*) is one of the largest and most impressive of the billfish. It ranges through temperate and tropical seas worldwide, usually in open waters.

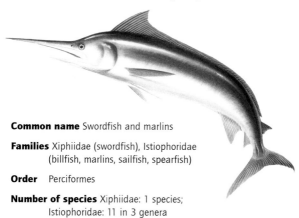

Common name Swordfish and marlins

Families Xiphiidae (swordfish), Istiophoridae (billfish, marlins, sailfish, spearfish)

Order Perciformes

Number of species Xiphiidae: 1 species; Istiophoridae: 11 in 3 genera

Size From about 6 ft (1.8 m) to 16.4 ft (5 m)

Key features All species elongate with a sword or bill: shortest in shortbill spearfish (*Tetrapturus angustirostris*); in swordfish (*Xiphias gladius*) sword is flattened from top to bottom and has sharp edges; in all other species sword is round in cross-section; body almost cylindrical in cross-section; eyes well formed; swordfish lack jaw teeth; dorsal fin narrow based in swordfish and long based in others; sail-like in sailfish (*Istiophorus* spp.); pelvic fins absent in swordfish, narrow but present in others; caudal peduncle has 1 keel on either side in swordfish and 2 keels in others; tail stiff, narrow, and well forked; coloration blackish fading to light brown or gray in swordfish; blue-black on back, shading to silvery flanks in marlins (*Makaira* spp.) and relatives; some species have vertical blue stripes

Breeding Generally occurs in relatively shallow water; single female may be courted by 1 or more males; millions of eggs produced in a single spawning

Diet Mainly fish, squid, and crustaceans

Habitat Open waters, including midocean; some species also frequent coastal waters; most remain in warmer surface waters above the thermocline

Distribution Most tropical and subtropical waters

Status IUCN lists swordfish as Data Deficient

Flounders

The bony ridge of this 40-inch (1-m) European plaice (*Pleuronectes platessa*) is visible behind its eyes. Lying flat on the rocky bottom of very shallow brackish or marine waters, it hunts for its favorite mollusks at night.

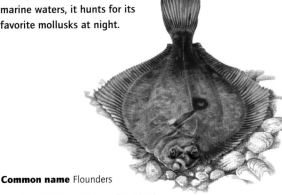

Common name Flounders

Families Bothidae (lefteye flounders),
Pleuronectidae (righteye flounders)

Order Pleuronectiformes

Number of species Bothidae: about 157 in 20 genera;
Pleuronectidae: nearly 120 in about 44 genera

Size From 1.4 in (3.5 cm) to 8.5 ft (2.6 m)

Key features Asymmetrical, oval-shaped bodies; head with both eyes on same (top) side; front edge of dorsal fin located above or in front of eyes; all fins separate from each other; pelvic fins asymmetrical in lefteyes, symmetrical in righteyes; coloration: top side heavily patterned in many species; capable of rapid color changes

Breeding About 2 million eggs released

Diet Invertebrates; larger species also take fish

Habitat Nearly always marine; Bothidae: tropical and temperate zones; usually over fine-grained bottoms; shallow or relatively shallow waters, normally above 330 ft (100 m); Pleuronectidae: tropical, subtropical, temperate, and (almost) Arctic zones; usually over fine-grained bottoms; depths above 660 ft (200 m); some species may enter brackish water

Distribution Atlantic, Indian, and Pacific Oceans;
Pleuronectidae: also Arctic Ocean

Status IUCN lists Atlantic halibut (*Hippoglossus hippoglossus*) as Endangered and yellowtail flounder (*Limanda ferriginea*) as Vulnerable

Soles

The 7.1-in (18-cm) drab sole (*Achirus achirus*), found on sandy or muddy bottoms of estuaries, rivers, and coastal streams, hides itself completely in sediment, leaving only its eyes visible.

Common name Soles

Families Soleidae (soles), Achiridae (American soles), Cynoglossidae (tongue soles or tonguefish)

Order Pleuronectiformes

Number of species Soleidae: over 120 in 26 genera; Achiridae: around 28 in 9 genera; Cynoglossidae: about 135 in 3 genera

Size From 0.8 inches (2 cm) to 43.3 in (110 cm)

Key features Oval-shaped bodies: from slim to relatively circular; asymmetrical with both eyes on same side of head; dorsal and anal fins very long-based; caudal fin separate in soles and American soles, continuous with dorsal and anal in tongue soles; pectoral fins absent in tongue soles; coloration: top side usually mottled or banded in various colors; bottom side white or light-colored

Breeding Eggs and sperm released into water, then abandoned

Diet Invertebrates; also fish

Habitat Soleidae: tropical to temperate zones; shallow or relatively shallow seas; some species inhabit deep water down to 4,430 ft (1,350 m), others in marine and brackish waters, a few in fresh water (especially fine-grained bottoms); Achiridae: tropical to temperate zones; primarily over fine-grained bottoms; most species marine, but many in brackish waters or fresh water; Cynoglossidae: tropical and subtropical zones; mainly deepwater marine and predominantly shallow water, from marine though brackish to fresh water

Distribution Soleidae: mainly European, African, Asian, and Australian seas; Achiridae: mostly both coasts of North and South America, also Indonesia, Australia, New Guinea, perhaps the Philippines; Cynoglossidae: most seas; not Arctic or Antarctic

Status Not threatened

Spikefish and Triplespines

The 3.3-inch (8.5-cm) shortsnout spikefish (*Triacanthodes ethiops*) is found in tropical waters at depths between 164 and 410 feet (50–125 m) in the Indo-West Pacific from South Africa eastward to Japan and south to Australia.

Common name Spikefish and triplespines

Families Triacanthodidae (spikefish), Triacanthidae (triplespines)

Order Tetraodontiformes

Number of species Triacanthodidae: about 21 in 11 genera; Triacanthidae: 7 in 4 genera

Size From 2 in (5 cm) to 12 in (30 cm)

Key features Elongated to deep body or deep at front, tapering to narrow caudal peduncle at back; some have long snouts with small mouths at tip, snout twisted to left or right; deep-bodied forms have small mouths, lack snouts; some have pointed head, small mouth at tip; eyes generally large, in some species set high on skull; prominent spines on dorsal fin, one on pelvic fin can be locked when raised; rounded tail fin or deeply forked; coloration: reddish or reddish-brown, fading to lighter color on belly; some have one or more thin bluish lines running along body (spikefish)

Breeding Eggs and sperm of triplespines released or scattered, then abandoned; larvae spend time among plankton

Diet Long-snouted species: soft, bottom-dwelling invertebrates (e.g., worms); "spoon-toothed": fish scales; also hard-shelled invertebrates (e.g., crustaceans) and bottom-living invertebrates

Habitat Shallow coastal waters down to about 360 ft (110 m), usually above 215 ft (65 m), or deep tropical or subtropical marine waters, down to 6,600 ft (2,000 m); some species in brackish water; longsnouted species over fine-grained bottoms; also sandy, muddy areas

Distribution Western Atlantic and Indo-Pacific

Status Not threatened

Triggerfish and Filefish

The 12-inch (30-cm) Picasso triggerfish (*Rhinecanthus aculeatus*) is commonly found in subtidal reef flats and shallow protected lagoons in the Indo-Pacific from the Red Sea down to South Africa and east to Hawaii.

Common name Triggerfish and filefish

Families Balistidae (triggerfish), Monacanthidae (filefish or leatherjackets)

Order Tetraodontiformes

Number of species Balistidae: 40 in about 11 genera; Monacanthidae: 104 in about 31 genera

Size From 1 in (2.5 cm) to 43.3 in (110 cm)

Key features Body usually compressed, roughly oval in shape; triggerfish body less deep, filefish covered in scales with several small spines on outer edge; mouth at tip of snout armed with powerful teeth; eyes set well back on head and toward top; 3 spines (2 in filefish) on first dorsal fin, last is very small; soft rays on second dorsal; well-formed caudal, often with extensions of topmost and lowermost rays; anal almost identical to second dorsal; pelvic fin has 1 spine and attached fold of skin; varied coloration: often spectacular, but sometimes unicolor in triggerfish

Breeding Eggs laid on site prepared by male; female triggerfish guard eggs, but males in filefish; some subtropical filefish release eggs in open water

Diet Sea urchins; also crustaceans (e.g., crabs), hard-shelled mollusks (e.g., snails), algae, worms, eggs, sea squirts, corals, zooplankton; also bottom-dwelling invertebrates

Habitat Most species tropical or subtropical, but some extend into more temperate areas; frequently associated with coral reefs and shallow water, usually less than 165 ft (50 m) deep; some filefish prefer sandy or other fine-grained bottoms or seagrass meadows

Distribution Atlantic, Indian, and Pacific Oceans

Status IUCN lists Queen triggerfish (*Balistes vetula*) as Vulnerable

Boxfish and Cowfish

The 18-inch (46-cm) longhorn cowfish (*Lactoria cornuta*) is found in the Red Sea east to Polynesia and north to Japan. It inhabits weedy areas near rocks or reefs at depths of between 60 and 330 feet (18–100 m).

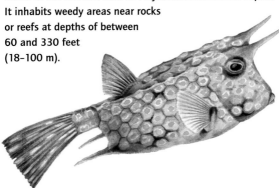

Common name Boxfish and cowfish

Family Ostraciidae (sometimes called Ostraciontidae)

Order Tetraodontiformes

Number of species 37 in 12 genera

Size 4.3 in (11 cm) to 21.7 in (55 cm)

Key features Body cubical or slightly longer and angular, encased in bony carapace or "shell" covered in thin, fleshy tissue; mouth small and partly beaklike; forehead may have hornlike projections; eyes located high on head; single dorsal fin placed well back on body, lacks hard spines; no pelvic skeleton or pelvic fins; coloration extremely variable and often bright: ranging from almost yellow all over to green with blue spots to deep-based colors highlighted with light spots

Breeding Most species have harem system of single male and several females; eggs released into water (often at dusk) and abandoned; hatching takes about 2 days

Diet Bottom-living invertebrates; also seagrasses

Habitat Mainly shallow-water reefs; some species found in seagrass meadows or sand, rocks, or rubble; members of subfamily Aracaninae prefer deeper waters down to 660 ft (200 m)

Distribution Tropical, subtropical, and sometimes temperate regions of Atlantic, Indian, and Pacific Oceans

Status Not threatened

Puffers and Porcupinefish

This 4.3-inch (11-cm) Valentinni's sharpnose puffer (*Canthigaster valentini*) lives among coral in lagoons and reefs.

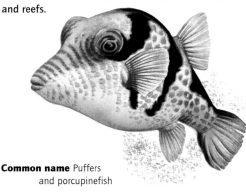

Common name Puffers and porcupinefish

Families Triodontidae (three-toothed puffer or pursefish), Tetraodontidae (puffers), Diodontidae (porcupinefish or burrfish)

Order Tetraodontiformes

Number of species Triodontidae: 1 in 1 genus; Tetraodontidae: 176 in 27 genera; Diodontidae: 20 in 7 genera

Size From 1.6 in (4 cm) to 48 in (1.2 m)

Key features Body elongated, almost spherical if inflated; roundly pointed snout, mouth at tip; fused jaw teeth project into beaklike structure: 2 fused teeth (porcupinefish), 3 (three-toothed puffer), 4 (other puffers); eyes high on head; body scaleless or short, pricklelike scales along belly (puffers), sharp spines (porcupinefish); belly with large purselike sac (three-toothed puffer); dorsal and anal fins set well back on body; no pelvic fins; coloration: variable, often brilliant, with spots and patches (puffers); belly "purse" has yellow ring circling prominent black "eye spot"; darker and lighter shades of brown (porcupinefish)

Breeding Spawn in groups in shallow nests in shallow beach areas after new and full moon; freshwater species spawn in pairs, male guards eggs or fry; eggs hatch in under 2 days or up to a month depending on species; planktonic larvae

Diet Invertebrates including sea urchins and starfish; also other fish and plants

Habitat Mostly marine: tropical or subtropical; or fresh brackish water; fine-grained to rocky bottoms; shallow water down to 1,000 ft (300 m)

Distribution Atlantic, Indian, and Pacific Oceans

Status IUCN lists 2 species as Vulnerable

Molas

The 11-foot (3.3-m) ocean sunfish (*Mola mola*) drifts at the surface while lying on its side or swims upright with its dorsal fin projecting above the water. It is believed the mola is the heaviest bony fish, up to 5,070 lb (2,300 kg), and produces the most eggs (300 million).

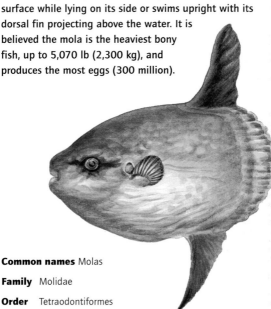

Common names Molas

Family Molidae

Order Tetraodontiformes

Number of species 4 in 3 genera

Size 40 in (1 m) to 11 ft (3.3 m)

Key features Scaleless body relatively compressed (i.e., flattened side to side), almost circular, but slightly elongated in some species; head rounded; small mouth with 2 fused jaw teeth; tiny nostrils on each side of head; eyes small; gill slits are small openings at base of pectoral fins; no pelvic fins or true caudal fin; dorsal and anal fins long and spineless; pseudo-tail formed from last rays of dorsal and anal fins; coloration: drab bluish-brown on back, fading to lighter shades down sides and along belly; brighter in some species

Breeding Vast numbers of small eggs produced, especially by large female ocean sunfish (*Mola mola*), which can produce 300 million or more; eggs and sperm scattered in open water, then abandoned; larvae with body spines that initially increase in number and are later absorbed

Diet Mainly jellyfish and other soft-bodied invertebrates; also crustaceans, sea urchins, fish, and seaweed

Habitat Open sea, usually close to surface; some species dive deeper, from 900 ft (300 m) down to 2,200 ft (760 m)

Distribution Tropical, subtropical, and warm temperate regions worldwide

Status Not threatened

Glossary

Words in SMALL CAPITALS refer to other entries in the glossary.

Abbreviated heterocercal term used to describe a HETEROCERCAL tail in which the upper LOBE is less extended than in a typical heterocercal tail

Adipose fin fatty FIN located behind rayed DORSAL FIN in some fish

Ammocete larva filter-feeding lamprey LARVA

Anadromous term describing a SPECIES that spends part of its life in the sea and part in freshwater habitats

Anal fin FIN located near the anus

Arborescent organ treelike modifications of GILL tissues found in air-breathing species like walking catfish

Atriopore small aperture in lancelets corresponding to the atrial, or exhalant, SIPHON in sea squirts

Barbel whiskerlike, sensory growth on the jaws of some fish, including catfish

Benthic occurring or living on the bottom

Benthopelagic occurring both at the bottom of the SUBSTRATE and in open sea

Brackish water that contains some salt but not as much as sea water; found in estuaries, mangrove swamps, and places where fresh water and sea water mix

Brood offspring of a single birth or clutch of eggs

Budding a form of asexual reproduction in which a new individual develops as a direct growth from the parent's body

Carapace the DORSAL shield of the external skeleton covering part of the body in most crustaceans

Cartilaginous formed of cartilage

Caudal fin "tail" FIN

Caudal peduncle part of the body where the tail begins

Chordata PHYLUM of animals having a single, hollow DORSAL nerve cord, GILL SLITS, a NOTOCHORD, and a postanal tail; some of these characteristics may only be present in early stages of development; animals in the Chordata are known as chordates

CITES Convention on International Trade in Endangered Species; an agreement between nations restricting international trade to permitted levels; rare animals and plants are assigned to categories

Class taxonomic level below PHYLUM and above ORDER

Cloaca single chamber into which anal, urinary, and genital ducts (canals) open

Colony a group of animals gathered together for breeding

Commensal living in close relationship with a member of another SPECIES; one benefits from the relationship, while the other neither benefits nor is harmed

Compressed flattened from side to side

Copepoda subclass of small crustaceans, some of which are parasitic; copepods do not have a CARAPACE (shell) but have a single, centrally placed eye

Countershading color distribution seen in many fish in which the back is darker than the belly

Cryptic coloration camouflage-type coloration that helps organisms blend in with their surroundings

Ctenoid scale similar to the CYCLOID SCALE but with a toothed rear edge rather than a smooth or wavy (crenulated) one

Cycloid scale thin, flexible overlapping SCALE found in modern bony fish and the primitive bowfin (*Amia calva*); the front edge of each scale is embedded in a special pouch in the surface of the skin; the back edge is free and smooth or wavy (crenulated) but not toothed

Demersal living near, deposited on, or sinking to the bottom of the sea

Denticle small, toothlike SCALE found in sharks and some of their closest relatives

Detritus debris consisting of fragments of dead plants and animals

Disk a flattened, rounded structure

Diurnal active during the day

Dorsal relating to the upper surface

Dorsal fin(s) FIN(S) on the back of a fish

Endangered species SPECIES whose POPULATION has fallen to such a low level that it is at risk of extinction

Erectile capable of being raised

Family group of closely related SPECIES or a pair of fish and their offspring

Fin winglike or paddlelike organ attached to certain parts of the body of a fish or other aquatic animal and used for steering, locomotion, and balance

Fry young fish

Ganoid scale SCALE found in most extinct ray-finned fish (Actinopterygii), consisting of a thick enamel-like layer underlaid by a dentine layer and a basal bony layer

Genus (pl. genera) group of closely related SPECIES

Gill organ by which a fish absorbs dissolved oxygen from the water and gets rid of carbon dioxide

Gill raker bristlelike extensions on the GILL arches of filter-feeding fish; used for trapping suspended food particles in the water as it passes from the mouth via the gills and, subsequently, to the exterior through the GILL SLITS

Gill slit slit between the GILLS that allows water to pass through

Gonopodium modified ANAL FIN of male LIVEBEARERS used to inseminate females

Gregarious living together in loose groups

Hermaphrodite organism having both male and female reproductive organs

Heterocercal term used to describe a tail (CAUDAL FIN) in which the upper LOBE contains the tip of the backbone; in such fins the upper lobe is usually considerably larger than the lower lobe

Internal fertilization fertilization in which the union of egg and sperm takes place inside the mother's body

IUCN International Union for the Conservation of Nature, responsible for assigning animals and plants to internationally agreed categories of rarity (see table on page 250)

Juvenile young animal that has not reached breeding age

Larva first stage of some fish SPECIES; newly hatched invertebrate

Larvacean small transparent animals belonging to the subphylum Urochordata

Lateral relating to the sides

Lateral line organ series of small fluid-filled pits linked to tubes that, in turn, are linked to a common canal; detects movements (vibrations) in the water

Livebearer SPECIES in which males introduce sperm into the body of the female, resulting in INTERNAL FERTILIZATION; developing embryos are generally retained by the female until birth

Lobe a rounded projection or division of a bodily part or organ

Median fins FINS located on lengthwise middle line of the body, e.g., DORSAL, CAUDAL, or ANAL fins

Mermaid's purse term used to describe the hard, leathery egg cases of sharks, skates, and rays

Metamorphosis changes undergone by an animal as it develops from the embryonic to the adult stage

Migration movement of animals from one part of the world to another at different times of the year to reach food or find a place to breed

Nocturnal active at night

Notochord "rod" of cells along the back during the early stages of embryonic development in chordates; it is replaced by the spinal column in all but the most primitive chordates (see CHORDATA)

Nuptial tubercle small, whitish, pimplelike growth developed by some males during the breeding season, usually on the snout, head, cheeks and PECTORAL FINS

Operculum bone forming the gill cover in fish

Orbital relating to the eyes

Order level of taxonomic ranking

Papilla (pl. papillae) small, usually cone-shaped projection

Pectoral fin one of the paired FINS connected to the pectoral girdle

Pelagic living in the water column as opposed to the bottom SUBSTRATE

Photophore luminous organ possessed by many deepwater bony and cartilaginous fish

Phylum (pl. phyla) group of animals whose basic or general plan is similar, and which share an evolutionary relationship, e.g., the CHORDATA

Placenta spongy, blood-rich tissue found in mammals and some fish, such as LIVEBEARING sharks, by which oxygen and nutrients are supplied to—and waste products are removed from—embryos during development

Plankton term used to describe the generally minute animals (zooplankton) and plants (phytoplankton) that drift in marine and fresh water

Polyp individual animal making up a COLONY, as in corals

Population distinct group of animals of the same SPECIES or all the animals of that species

Proboscis elongated trunklike snout or projection

Pterygiophores the bones or cartilages that connect with the base of the RAYS of the MEDIAN FINS

Ray small spine that acts as a support for the FIN membrane

Rostral associated with a rostrum (snout)

Scale one of the usually tough, flattish plates that form part of the external covering of most fish SPECIES

Schooling behavior involving a large number of fish of one kind swimming together

Scute platelike, modified SCALES found in some fish, including catfish

Sessile unable to move around

Siphon funnel-shaped structure through which water can be taken in (inhalant) or discharged (exhalant)

Spawn eggs of a fish; the act of producing eggs

Species a POPULATION or series of populations that interbreed freely but not normally with those of other species

Spiracle porelike opening associated with the GILLS

Substrate bottom of an aquatic habitat

Subterminal located underneath the end or tip, e.g., a subterminal mouth is located underneath the tip of the snout

Suprabranchial chamber cavity or space above the GILL chamber; houses the modified gill tissues used by air-breathing fish

Swim bladder gas-filled sac found in the body cavity of most bony fish; the amount of gas in the swim bladder can be regulated, allowing the fish to rise or sink in the water

Tendril entwining, fiberlike extension on some shark and ray egg cases that allows the eggs to attach themselves to underwater objects such as seaweeds

Territory area that an animal or animals consider their own and defend against others

Test an external covering or "shell" of an invertebrate, especially sea squirts; it is in fact an internal skeleton just below the skin

Thermocline zone between warm surface water and colder deeper layers

Tubercle small rounded swelling, nodule, or protuberance, as found, e.g., on the body of banjo catfish

Ventral relating to the underside

Vestigial a characteristic with little or no contemporary use, but derived from one that was useful and well developed in an ancestral form

Visceral cleft the area consisting of the jaw, hyoid (the bone at the base of the tongue) and the GILL arches

Viviparous producing live offspring

Yolk sac source of nourishment for some FRY prior to and immediately after hatching

Zooplankton see PLANKTON

IUCN CATEGORIES

EX **Extinct,** when there is no reasonable doubt that the last individual of the species has died.

EW **Extinct in the Wild,** when a species is known only to survive in captivity or as a naturalized population well outside the past range.

CR **Critically Endangered,** when a species is facing an extremely high risk of extinction in the wild in the immediate future.

EN **Endangered,** when a species is facing a very high risk of extinction in the wild in the near future.

VU **Vulnerable,** when a species is facing a high risk of extinction in the wild in the medium-term future.

LR **Lower Risk** (before 2001)**/NT Near Threatened** (since 2001), when a species has been evaluated and does not satisfy the criteria for CR, EN, or VU.

LC **Least Concern** (since 2001), when an animal has been evaluated and does not qualify for CR, EN, VU, LR, or NT.

DD **Data Deficient,** when there is not enough information about a species to assess the risk of extinction.

NE **Not Evaluated,** species that have not been assessed by the IUCN criteria.

Index

Bold common names and page numbers, e.g. **aba aba 81**, indicate a fish that has its own illustrated main entry. Other bold numbers indicate a fish or group of fish that is the subject of the main entry. Page numbers in italics, e.g. *172*, indicate illustration of a member of the group that is the subject of the main entry.